2180

621.43
Olney, Ross
    Internal combustion engines.

Date Due

internal-
combustion
engines

internal-combustion engines

by ross olney

THOMAS NELSON INC.

To Chan Bush,
one of the most skilled
of all the racing and motor
photographers in the business,
and a good friend.

acknowledgments

The author would like to thank the following, who helped with advice, technical information, photos, and diagrams: Chan Bush, Photographer; Dan Chabek, Ford Motor Company; Kent Bowerly, Tollycraft Corporation; Will Rusch, McCulloch Corporation; Jack MacFarland, Dodge News Bureau; Frederick C. Tew, Chrysler Corporation; R. L. Norwood, Chrysler-Plymouth Division; Dick Klawitter, Kiekhaefer Mercury; Johnson Motors; Larry L. Strain, American Airlines; Sebastion S. Attardo, American Airlines; United States Coast Guard; Triumph Corporation; Al Bloemker, Indianapolis Motor Speedway; Bultaco Western; James Jingu, Yamaha International; Eric Rickman, *Hot Rod* Magazine; Champion Spark Plug Company; Vince Granatelli, Paxton Products; Robert McKee, Ford Motor Company Lima Engine Plant; Sol London, Lockheed-California Company; H. A. Wheeler, Firestone Tire and Rubber Company; Deke Houlgate, Riverside International Raceway; and Harvey Aluminum Company.

contents

internal-combustion engines

basic principles

"Gentlemen, start your engines!"

Spoken by the president of the Indianapolis Motor Speedway Corporation, these words order thirty-three of the finest racing-car drivers in the entire world to begin one of the most exciting, noisy, dangerous events in all of sports.

Short moments later, the racers will thunder away for a hazardous 500-mile run for riches in the famous Indianapolis Speedway Race. For immediately upon the command from the Speedway president, who stands in the rear seat of the convertible pace car, mechanics shove electric starting motors into starting gears, and a staccato rumble fills the air as one by one the engines start. Soon all are running, then slowly and carefully the pace car pulls away from the starting line and into the first turn of the grand old two-and-a-half-mile oval track.

Picking up speed, the standard passenger car used as the pace car is soon traveling "wide open" around the curves and down the backstretch. Eighty miles per hour . . . then ninety . . . then one hundred miles per hour the pace car screams, still picking up speed.

Behind it, the low-slung, gleaming little racers are aligned in rows, three across and eleven deep. The drivers appear almost nonchalant, some still donning gloves or lowering goggles, for these machines are

After "Gentlemen, start your engines!" comes the thrilling start of the annual 500-mile race at the Indianapolis Motor Speedway. These are thirty-three of the finest internal-combustion engines in the world in fast and rough action. (Courtesy Indianapolis Motor Speedway)

merely loafing along behind the pace car. A few of the drivers wave at the fans as they pass by on their parade and pace laps.

Engines rumbling deeply with a sound that indicates the power soon to be unleashed, the racers follow their leader through the last turn of the final pace lap and onto the main straightaway. The drivers are by now intent, staring ahead at the starting line, waiting for the drop of the green flag by the official starter.

In the pace car, sitting and holding tightly to the seat as the automobile approaches its maximum speed, the president and the official observers glance to the rear for a final check on the alignment of the following racers. They are perfectly lined up according to their qualification positions.

Everything seems ready.

Swerving sharply to the left, the driver of the pace car careens along a ramp and into the pits, opening the track ahead. At the same instant, the starter wildly waves a green flag high over his head—and in that second, pandemonium reigns.

Every single driver stabs his accelerator to the floor, and the deep rumble of engines turns to a screaming roar as each car strains for speed. It is the most critical, the most thrilling, the most dangerous moment in all of sports. The sound of these thundering engines stands the hair on end, brings chills to the spine—and often tears to the eyes of the true engine lover, for he is hearing near-perfection in engines.

As every modern internal-combustion engine has been built for a single purpose, so have these racing engines been built. Each part has been selected with care, or machined from a chunk of metal for a specific purpose. Microscopic tolerances have been followed; then, when the part is ready for installation, it is once again examined by X-ray machines. This will uncover any hidden flaws or cracks that cannot be seen by human eyes. Lovingly experts assemble each engine, taking precise care in every single operation, for this engine will be called upon to operate at great speeds and under tremendous stresses.

Even then, at the end of 500 grinding miles of racing, many of them will be nothing but junk. A few will crash into the unyielding walls of

14

"Indy." Others will burst apart under the terrible pounding, and others will fail because of some small undetected internal weakness.

Thousands of small parts make up the modern racing engine, and the modern passenger-car engine. As a matter of fact, in spite of the difference of their primary job, the two are much alike. And each is similar in basic design and operation to the modern aircraft internal-combustion engine and the modern marine engine—and even to the modern motorcycle engine. They all work in the same basic way.

The gasoline engine performs its work by burning a mixture of gasoline vapor and air inside a cylinder, which is a part of the engine. For this reason, the unit is known as an *internal*-combustion engine. When the fuel-air mixture burns, hot gases are formed. It is the rapid expansion of these burning gases that moves the piston of the engine and turns the crankshaft.

The spinning crankshaft can then be connected to whatever is to be driven, such as the wheels (through the transmission) of a standard automobile or race car or truck, or the propeller of an airplane, or the screw of a boat, or even the pump of a well or the generator of a power plant.

The physicist would say that the internal combustion engine changes heat energy into mechanical energy. The rate at which the engine produces work is usually measured in *horsepower*.

Diagram shows external- and internal-combustion engines. (Courtesy Ford Motor Company)

INTERNAL COMBUSTION ENGINE   EXTERNAL COMBUSTION ENGINE

The modern internal-combustion engine is very light in weight for the amount of energy it can produce, making it the primary type of engine for all vehicles today. Though somewhat different in operation, both the diesel engine and the turbine engine are also internal-combustion types that change heat energy into mechanical energy. There will be more about them in a later chapter.

What about the steam engine? Does it not also convert heat energy into mechanical energy, and thus become one of the group? No; a steam engine is operated from heat from another source, usually from a fire under a boiler completely apart from the energy-producing part of the engine. This type would be what is known as an *external*-combustion engine (the burning is not inside the cylinders, though the results are similar).

Do you remember the pirate movies that thrilled us all as youngsters? The sleek pirate ship, in the final scenes, would ease up alongside a victim and prepare for a "broadside," and, depending upon which ship the hero commanded, we knew that somebody was soon going to go to the bottom of the sea.

"Beat general quarters!" The command would be snapped from the bridge, and seamen would rush to their stations by the old cannons.

"Make ready to fire!" would be the next command, and quickly powder, wadding, and shot would be shoved down the barrels of the cannons. As quickly as this was done, another sailor would step forward and "ram" the shot and charge, packing it tightly into the closed end of the cannon.

"Fire!" the captain would shout, and all along the row of cannons men would step forward with lighted torches, touch the fire to the fuses, and the powder inside the cannons would almost instantly burn, forcing the heavy cannon balls to shoot from the mouth of the cannons. Quickly, without even watching to see where the balls had struck, other men would then step forward and "swab" the cannon barrels to clean them and to extinguish any burning powder left inside.

Just substitute the cannon barrel for a cylinder inside an internal-combustion engine, the powder and wadding for fuel, the cannon ball for a piston, the torch for a spark plug, and the swabbing for the exhaust stroke, and you have the basic action of a modern engine.

At the "make ready" command, the gasoline vapor is entering the cylinder and the piston is closing the space inside. Finally the piston "rams" the fuel into the smallest possible space and at that instant it "fires." Not a man with a torch, of course, but a spark plug ignites the compressed fuel mixture.

The fuel burns rapidly, expanding hot gases inside the cylinder and driving the piston back with great force, just as the cannon drove the ball from its mouth with force enough to make it fly between ships. In the modern engine, this forceful motion of the piston turns the crankshaft, and drives the automobile forward through a series of gears in the transmission.

Finally, in the automobile engine, the piston travels the other way in the cylinder again, this time to "swab" the "barrel" by pushing burned gases into the exhaust system. As the piston comes back from this action on its continuing back-and-forth or up-and-down motions, new fuel is drawn in and the entire cycle is repeated.

This fuel we burn in our modern internal-combustion engines is manufactured from petroleum, which has been stored deep within the earth for millions of years in the form of crude oil. It contains the concentrated energy of the sun, and it is this energy we are finally using. The potential energy in gasoline, in fact, is far greater than that in TNT, nitroglycerin, or dynamite. Gasoline contains three times as much energy as TNT, six times as much as nitroglycerin, and nearly eight times as much energy as top-grade dynamite.

Consider it this way. With one gallon of gasoline in a well-tuned engine we can drive an average car on a smooth stretch of highway for a distance of perhaps eighteen miles. Yet if we were to substitute pure nitroglycerin for the gasoline in the tank, we could only go about three miles on one gallon.

With all this talk of nitroglycerin and other explosives, we must not forget that, in the case of the gun and in the case of the engine, the fuel inside *burns*—it does not *explode*. We even add materials to gasoline to

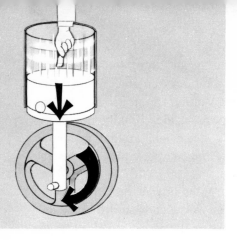

In an internal-combustion engine, the piston is *pushed* rather than slammed in the cylinder. (Courtesy Ford Motor Company)

make it burn slower than it normally would. If the gasoline-air mixture inside the cylinder of an engine exploded, it would be just like hitting the top of the piston with a sledge hammer; and this would not do the job at all. In short order the engine would be knocking and rattling and finally it would just fall apart. Where *exploding* fuel would *strike* the piston, *burning* fuel exerts a *push* against the piston.

Tetraethyl lead is one material added to better gasolines to slow the burning, giving us ethyl-grade fuel.

This does not mean that the burning inside a cylinder is slow. It all happens in a split second, much too fast to be noted if we could look inside an engine while it is running. The top space of each cylinder would merely glow with fire, and we would be unable to tell exactly when the gasoline is burning and when it is not—but still it is not exploding.

Sea water and a dash of table salt might be the last things you would consider dropping into your gasoline tank on the family car, but these are only a couple of the many ingredients used to make modern anti-knock gasoline for internal-combustion engines. Obviously the heavy, black, thick crude oil that comes up from an oil well would not work in an engine, so this petroleum is run through the cracking process or the "Rexforming" method to break it down and to produce pure gasoline, then to this purified product are added the other materials to further improve it for engine use.

One of the greatest problems facing early-day engineers, just after the automobile engine was invented, was the "knocking" in the engine each time they tried to build a more powerful model. No matter what they did, the knock would build to an unbearable level, finally shaking the engine apart.

Although many engineers thought that the ignition system was the villain, scientists Charles F. Kettering and Thomas Midgley suspected the fuel, and they set about to develop an antiknock gasoline. They even placed a window in the side of an engine so that they could try to watch the gasoline burning inside. In a major breakthrough in engine development (and, of course, in fuel development) they learned that the gasoline was burning too fast. They slowed the action by adding the tetraethyl compounds they developed, and the knock disappeared. This fuel first went on sale at gasoline stations in Dayton, Ohio, in 1923.

Since then, many other compounds have been developed and added to gasoline, with each oil company claiming its own compounds to be best. Today we are bombarded with advertisements on television and everywhere we look, each suggesting that a particular gasoline brand is best because of the secret additives used.

They are all good enough, to be sure, but most of us have also learned to take claims of superiority with a grain of salt—and not in the gasoline

Stock-car racing is another popular application of the internal-combustion engine. Here Dan Gurney screams around Turn 6 at Riverside International Raceway. (Chan Bush)

Other applications of the standard internal-combustion engine:

A. The famed Dodge "Little Red Wagon" does a wheel-stand. (Dodge News Bureau);

B. Tommy Ivo, TV actor, used *four* engines in his high-powered drag racer. (Tommy Ivo photo);

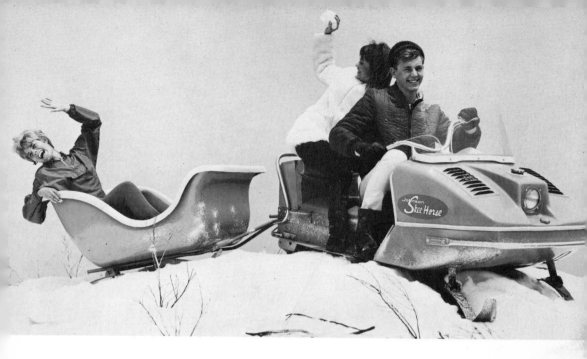

C. Snowmobiles, powered by internal-combustion engines, are great winter fun. (Courtesy Johnson Motors);

D. Chain saws cut the work way down, this one shown in a cutaway view. (Courtesy McCulloch Corporation);

An internal-combustion engine-powered welder is hauled up the famed Eiffel Tower in Paris. (Courtesy McCulloch Corporation)

tank. We do have one fairly sure method of telling the real quality of gasoline, aside from trying to test each and every one in the family car.

We can note the octane rating of gasolines, a government-controlled method of measurement. That is, no oil company may claim that their gasoline is of a higher octane than it actually is.

The octane number is a rating given gasolines of different quality, the higher the better (or more powerful). The rating number indicates the antiknock qualities of the fuel and the power of the fuel. It works like this. Gasoline is made up of hydrogen and carbon atoms combined into various kinds of molecules called *hydrocarbons*. One of these hydrocarbons, called *normal heptane* (C_7H_{16}), has such a tendency to knock in an internal-combustion engine that it has been given an octane rating of zero.

E. More working applications of the internal-combustion engine. (Courtesy McCulloch Corporation)

Another hydrocarbon is *iso-octane* and it, burned alone in an internal-combustion engine, has so *little* tendency to knock that it has been given a rating of 100.

A blend of the two would then have a certain rating, depending upon how much of each was used. *Regular*-grade gasoline has an average octane rating of about 90, while *premium*-grade gasoline rates about 100. Then to each grade of gasoline is added the tetraethyl-lead compounds to inhibit knocks even more and to increase the octane rating of the fuel. Aircraft engines, for example, require gasoline with an octane rating well above 100.

So-called "white" gasoline is unleaded, does not contain tetraethyl-lead compounds, and so is very low in octane rating.

Diagram and two views of the "Goldenrod," a high-speed Salt Flats car with *four* internal-combustion engines. (Courtesy Wayne Thoms)

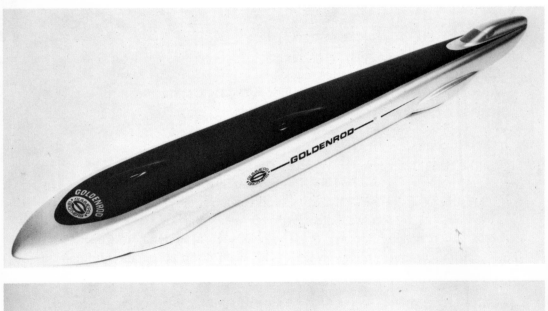

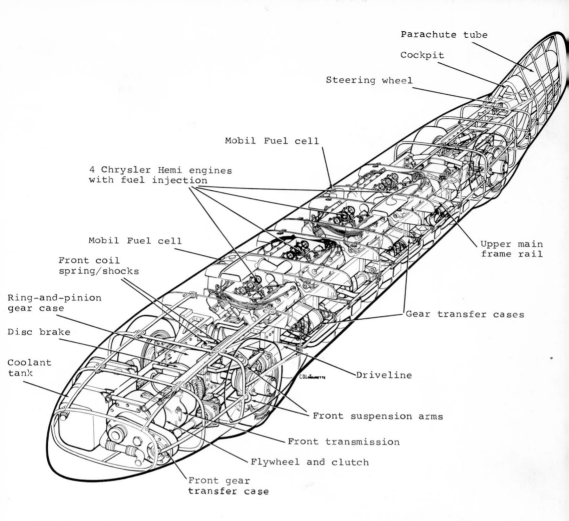

Parachute tube

Cockpit

Steering wheel

Mobil Fuel cell

4 Chrysler Hemi engines
with fuel injection

Mobil Fuel cell

Front coil
spring/shocks

Ring-and-pinion
gear case

Disc brake

Coolant
tank

Upper main
frame rail

Gear transfer cases

Driveline

Front suspension arms

Front transmission

Flywheel and clutch

Front gear
transfer case

Which gasoline should you use in your engine? That depends upon the size and power of the engine, for many engines work better on a lower-octane fuel, or at least work as well as they do on one rated higher. In fact, if you were to put aviation fuel in your gasoline tank, you might well ruin your engine, for the octane rating would be far too high.

Primarily, your choice will depend upon whether your engine has "low compression" or "high compression."

25

classification of engines

When the fuel in your engine burns and pushes the piston inside the cylinder, mechanical energy has been developed from heat energy. This energy, or power, is transmitted through the crankshaft to whatever it is you wish to run. And this power will be in direct proportion to the amount of expansion of burning gas in the cylinder.

That is, if the volume of gas expanding is small, then the power developed will be low, while if the gas increases in a much greater volume, the power developed and the work performed will be proportionately higher.

This is known as the "expansion ratio" and will equal the better-known "compression ratio," the difference in volume before and after compression. The more efficient an engine is, the higher will be its expansion ratio, as a general rule. If the burning gasoline-air mixture inside the cylinder expands to twice its size while burning, the engine is said to have a ratio of 2 to 1; if three times its former size in volume, the ratio is 3 to 1.

Since the expansion ratio will equal the compression ratio in a given cylinder or engine (remember, they are the same, though one expresses the state of the fuel mixture after ignition while the other is before) then these engines would have a compression ratio of 2 to 1 or 3 to 1, also. These would be very low-compression engines, perhaps early-day engines that burned very low-octane fuel.

This race-car engine is a high-compression model. (Chan Bush)

27

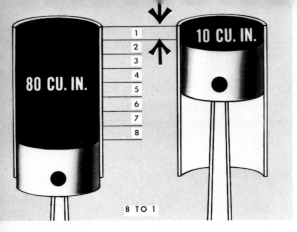

80 CU. IN.

10 CU. IN.

8 TO 1

Compression-ratio diagram (Courtesy Ford Motor Company)

Today's low-compression engines have ratios of at least 6 or 8 to 1, and burn higher-octane gasoline. And even in these modern internal-combustion engines, fuel with too high an octane rating will ruin them, or at the very best will be a great waste of money since the higher the octane the higher the price of the gasoline.

Bearing in mind that the compression ratio of an engine expresses the actual difference between the volume of the fuel mixture inside the cylinder before and after (or at the very instant of) ignition, today's modern high-compression engines have a ratio of at least 10 to 1 and probably 12 to 1. The fuel-air mixture is actually compressed by the piston down to one twelfth its size before ignition (compression ratio, 12 to 1) and expands then to twelve times its compressed size (expansion ratio, 12 to 1) as it burns, imparting great energy to the moving piston and the turning crankshaft.

Simply stated, the higher the compression ratio, the more powerful and more efficient the engine—and the more expensive.

Obviously, the engines used in the racers at Indianapolis are very, very high-compression units using a very high-octane fuel to develop their great power and speed. This, in fact, is why you often hear manufacturers of "Indy" cars advertise that certain parts of their engines are "stock" (depending upon whether they win or break apart, of course). A stock engine or engine part is just like a part you might use in your own automobile engine—an off-the-shelf item. Since it is possible, with unlimited money and time and skill, to develop a very high-bred engine that could sustain such high speeds over such a long distance, the engine

28

might mean little to the general public except for the excitement it causes on the race track. But if stock parts or engines are used, it could mean a great deal to the public, for this could be an engine that they themselves might use. If a stock engine or engine part could take such a terrible

A very high-compression internal-combustion engine (with supercharger) mounted on a dragster. (Chan Bush photo)

beating on the race track and then come back for more, think how well it would perform in an average automobile—or so the racing men figure when they advertise any stock parts they have used for racing.

Gasoline engines are classified (1) by their compression ratios, (2) by the number of piston strokes per cycle, (3) by the way they are cooled, (4) by their valve arrangement, (5) by their cylinder arrangement, and (6) by the way they are supplied with air and fuel. We will consider first the number of piston strokes per cycle.

All gasoline engines of the piston type operate on either the two-stroke-cycle principle or the four-stroke-cycle principle. These need not be confusing and in fact they become quite obvious, once explained.

Take a small model-airplane engine, something you can hold in your hand. As it turns out, this will be very similar to the engines that power your automobile or the huge trucks you see on the highways or even the "Indy" engines we have been following, at least in basic operation. The only major differences will be in size, of course, and in the fact that it is a two-stroke-cycle engine.

First, we break down the term "two-stroke-cycle." A *stroke* is the up-and-down movement of the piston inside the cylinder. *Cycle* is the series of steps that must be repeated from one ignition of fuel to the next. So obviously a two-stroke-cycle engine would mean an engine in which the piston only goes down and then comes back up (two strokes) between ignitions of the fuel in the combustion area of the cylinder. This is what happens inside the little model-airplane engine.

The fuel ignites and burns, pushing the piston down and, in this case, turning the tiny crankshaft that spins the propeller. One stroke. But then a great deal happens inside this little engine, and it all happens in a split second.

As the piston reaches BDC (bottom dead center) the burned gases are already exhausting through a port in the side of the cylinder that has been uncovered by the downward movement of the piston (see illustration). With the engine moving in a very exaggerated slow motion, let's watch what happens to the piston as the exhaust gases flow out. It starts back up inside the cylinder, driven now by the force of the moving crankshaft. As it rises, new fuel enters from another port, usually on the opposite side of the cylinder from the exhaust port and also opened by the uncovering action of the piston. The fuel is drawn into this very simple little engine by the outflowing of the exhaust gases, which is creating suction. The piston moves up higher and higher in the cylinder and finally closes off both ports, sealing the new fuel inside. It continues to rise, compressing the fuel, and as it reaches the top of the cylinder a spark plug ignites the compressed fuel mixture. The fuel burns, forcing the piston down in the cylinder. This entire action is repeated again and again, faster than the mind can comprehend, and the engine screams and spins the propeller at very high speeds.

This type of engine is lubricated by oil mixed with the gasoline, and ignited (in most cases) by a "glow plug" which is hot all the time— though certain of these very small model engines are actually timed to fire at the proper point of piston travel, and have a tiny timing mechanism to accomplish this. Many motorcycle engines operate on this two-stroke-cycle principle and they, being larger, are all equipped with timing devices rather than glow plugs, thus using normal spark plugs.

Diagram of a four-stroke-cycle engine operation. (Courtesy McCulloch Corporation)

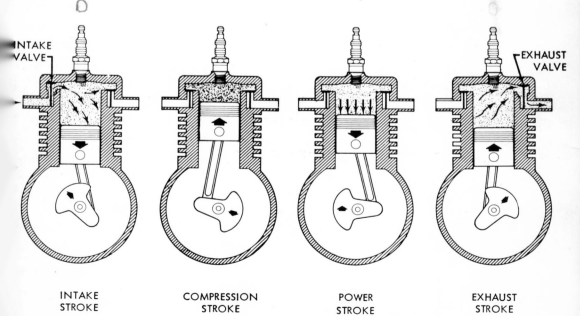

INTAKE VALVE   EXHAUST VALVE

| INTAKE STROKE | COMPRESSION STROKE | POWER STROKE | EXHAUST STROKE |

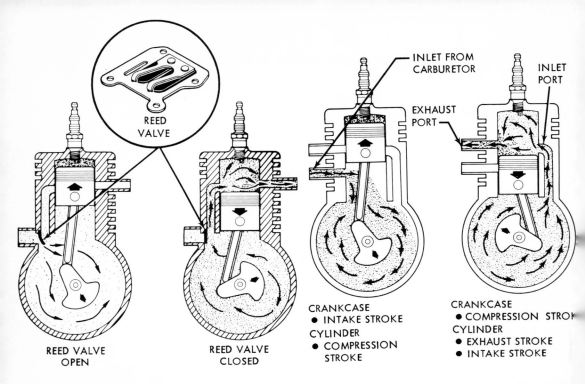

INLET FROM
CARBURETOR

INLET
PORT

EXHAUST
PORT

REED
VALVE

REED VALVE
OPEN

REED VALVE
CLOSED

CRANKCASE
● INTAKE STROKE
CYLINDER
● COMPRESSION
STROKE

CRANKCASE
● COMPRESSION STROKE
CYLINDER
● EXHAUST STROKE
● INTAKE STROKE

Two diagrams of a two-stroke-cycle operation: (*Left*) uses the most common "reed" valve; (*Right*) standard valve ports which are opened and closed by piston action. (Courtesy McCulloch Corporation)

Two-stroke-cycle engines are not as efficient as four-stroke-cycle engines, but they are much simpler and cheaper to build, and they do have a greater "power-to-weight" ratio. That is, they do actually develop more power for their much lighter weight.

Being smaller and lighter and cheaper, these engines are quite often used for power lawnmowers, light motorcycles, and other applications where low cost with no great speed or endurance is required.

A *four*-stroke-cycle engine, more complicated, has intake, compression, power, and exhaust strokes—*four* strokes between ignitions. This is the engine in your car, though for the moment we will still consider a one-cylinder engine, such as those in the little Honda motorcycle. For one thing, this engine is more complicated since *valves* are required, and since there must be at least one *camshaft* in the engine. Here's how this one works.

As the piston travels downward with the expansion of the burning fuel, the crankshaft is turned. Both valves are closed and the combustion chamber is sealed. But now we have a sealed chamber full of burned gases that have been expended of their power. So the next stroke of the piston as it moves from bottom dead center back toward the closed end of the cylinder will clear the chamber and prepare it for the next power stroke. As the piston moves upward in the cylinder, the exhaust valve opens and the gases are forced out through this opening. The piston goes all the way to the top of the cylinder, just as though preparing for another power stroke. But when it reaches the top the spark plug does not fire, for it would do no good. There is no compressed fuel waiting to burn.

So the piston starts back down again (moved by the force of the spinning crankshaft, which still has great inertia) on the third of its four strokes. Immediately, almost instantaneously, the exhaust valve snaps shut and the *intake* valve opens. The suction of the piston traveling in the cylinder draws in a fresh supply of the fuel-air mixture provided by the carburetor. Then the piston starts up again on the last of its four strokes. This time it compresses the fuel mixture, for the intake valve now closes. At the top, the spark plug ignites the compressed mixture and the piston is forced down on the first stroke of the next cycle.

It is almost impossible to imagine just how fast these operations occur, for the end result is a roar of power as the ignition and burning noise

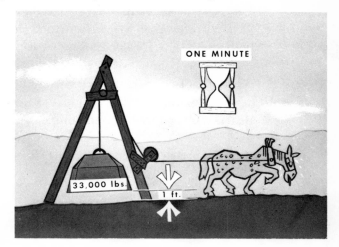

Diagram illustrating horsepower.
(Courtesy Ford Motor Company)

ONE MINUTE

33,000 lbs.

1 ft.

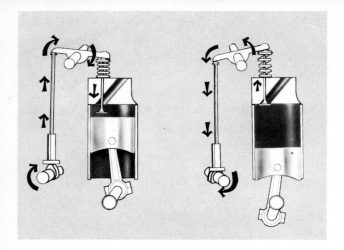

Diagram illustrating camshaft, push-rod, rocker-arm, and valve operation. (Courtesy Ford Motor Company)

blends (even in a one-cylinder engine) to a steady sound. Lubrication in a four-stroke-cycle engine is provided from an oil reservoir inside the engine called the "oil pan" or "oil sump." A pump forces oil up and onto the moving parts, the driving action of the pump coming from the engine itself.

The force in both two- and four-stroke-cycle engines is measured in horsepower, a measurement of just how much work is being produced by the running engine. Obviously, increasing the number of cylinders from one to two, or four, or eight, will increase the final output of the engine, and that is just what automobile builders have done. Still, each cylinder in the engine goes through the steps (or cycles) described.

Horsepower, as a means of measuring the output of an engine, was developed by James Watt (the man who invented a better steam engine). Watt compared the work done by an engine with the work a strong draft horse was able to do. He concluded that the horse could deliver 33,000 foot-pounds of work in one minute. One foot-pound equals one pound raised one foot. Thus one horsepower is defined as 33,000 foot-pounds of work per minute.

If an engine is able to move a resistance of 33,000 pounds for a distance of one foot in one minute, it is said to be a one-horsepower (1-

Six self-explanatory diagrams showing different engine parts in a one-cylinder unit. (Courtesy Ford Motor Company)

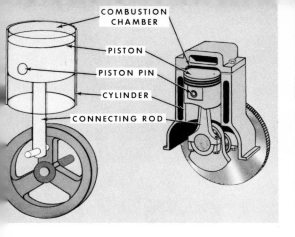

COMBUSTION CHAMBER

PISTON

PISTON PIN

CYLINDER

CONNECTING ROD

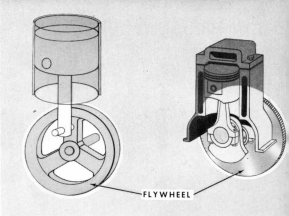

FLYWHEEL

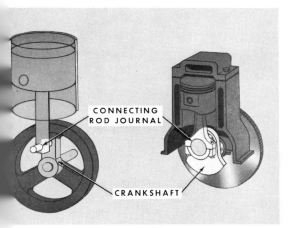

CONNECTING ROD JOURNAL

CRANKSHAFT

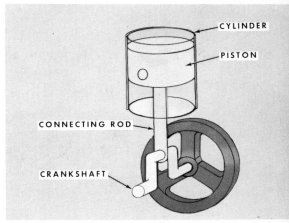

CYLINDER

PISTON

CONNECTING ROD

CRANKSHAFT

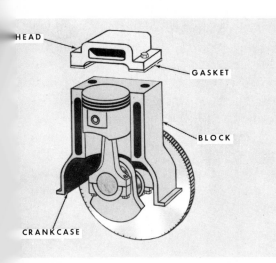

HEAD

GASKET

BLOCK

CRANKCASE

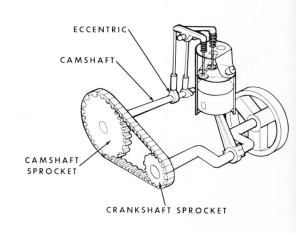

ECCENTRIC

CAMSHAFT

CAMSHAFT SPROCKET

CRANKSHAFT SPROCKET

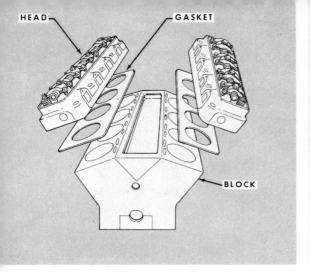

HEAD · GASKET · BLOCK

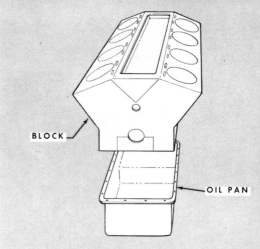

BLOCK · OIL PAN

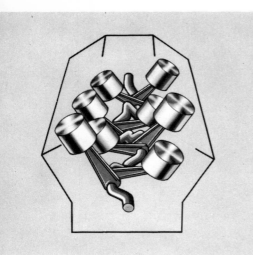

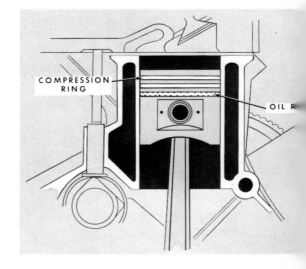

COMPRESSION RING · OIL R

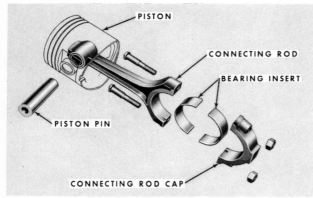

PISTON · CONNECTING ROD · BEARING INSERT · PISTON PIN · CONNECTING ROD CAP

Five self-explanatory diagrams showing different engine parts in an eight-cylinder engine. (Courtesy Ford Motor Company)

Spark-plug diagram. (Courtesy Ford Motor Company)

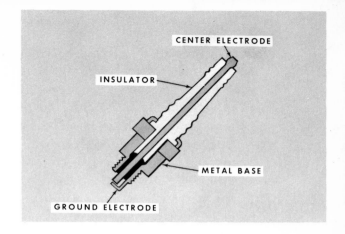

hp) engine. Or, if it can move the same amount of resistance for the same distance in one half minute, it is called a two-horsepower engine. The little model-airplane engine we discussed very likely had a horsepower rating of only a small fraction of one horsepower, while the modern automobile engine has a rating of several *hundred* horsepower.

A man can have horsepower too, though the measurements are small. If, for example, a 175-pound man climbs to a height of 75 feet, he does 13,125 foot-pounds of work ($175 \times 75 = 13,125$). If he makes the climb in one minute, he will have exerted .39 horsepower, or 13,125 divided by 33,000. A man accustomed to hard work can continuously exert one tenth to one eighth horsepower in an eight-hour day.

The *indicated* horsepower of a modern engine is calculated according to the work done on the pistons by the gases produced by ignition. The average gas pressure on the piston is multiplied by the area of the piston, the length of the piston stroke in feet, and the number of piston strokes per minute. The resulting figure will be in foot-pounds per minute, and this is then divided by 33,000 foot pounds per minute to give the engine's horsepower rating.

The *brake* horsepower or *effective* horsepower of an internal-combustion engine is an actual measurement of the amount of work the engine can do or, for example, the actual amount of power applied to the transmission of an automobile. This is measured by an instrument known as a *dynamometer,* which records the actual turning force of the final drive shaft of the engine. This figure is sometimes different from advertised figures, for where engineers like to know the *actual* amount of work the engine can do under operating conditions, the advertising men like to stretch a point to make the engine look good. The truth is, the horsepower of an engine can be calculated on a *stripped* engine (which is not even expending some of its power to drive its own fan, and water pump, and oil pump, and generator or alternator, or other necessary accessories). All of these items, which under normal conditions are driven by the engine along with the chore of powering the car, can be mounted externally and driven by another engine so that the engine being measured can be made to appear that it is putting out far more power than it actually is. Effective horsepower is an engineering term and is generally a true indication of the output of an engine under actual operating conditions, for the engine in your car will certainly have to drive all the accessories (water pump, fuel pump, generator, and so on) that keep it running smoothly and efficiently, as well as the wheels of the car.

Bear in mind also that these accessories are all internal or external engine components, actual parts of the engine. Other accessory items have a great effect on the final amount of power delivered to the wheels of the car, but these items cannot fairly be taken into consideration when figuring the horsepower of an engine, for they are in no way necessary to the operation of the engine. An automobile air conditioner, for example, can pull up to fifteen horsepower from an engine, and even the lights, horn, radio, and other such minor items, do pull a tiny amount of the horsepower that would normally be delivered to the wheels.

engine assembly and operation

A modern engine-manufacturing plant is an amazing operation. Man has progressed to the point where he can build factories to manufacture engines that are almost untouched by human hands. The Ford Motor Company, for example, has such a plant in Lima, Ohio. It is a sprawling complex of machines and overhead conveyor belts and quality-control measuring devices which all mesh together through a final "hot-test" line and onto a shipping dock where railroad cars await loading.

Into certain doors on one side of the plant come castings and forgings and other metal and plastic parts. Into other doors come premanufactured parts (made at other factories), such as spark plugs, oil pumps, water pumps, and small accessory parts. Everything is either hooked to a belt, or shipped to the department where the parts will be used. Buttons are pushed, and the whole plant comes alive.

Heavy castings are carried overhead to certain machines where they are automatically lowered into place and drilled or bored or milled or honed, or any combination of operations. Then, again automatically, they are raised, moved to the next operation, and lowered again. Between certain critical operations are quality-control machines and men. The part is lowered into one of these machines and in a split second hundreds of measurements are made and recorded. If the part passes the inspection, it is raised and sent on to the next operation. If it fails, it is ejected from the machine onto another conveyor that takes it back to be reworked or scrapped (depending upon the severity of the failure).

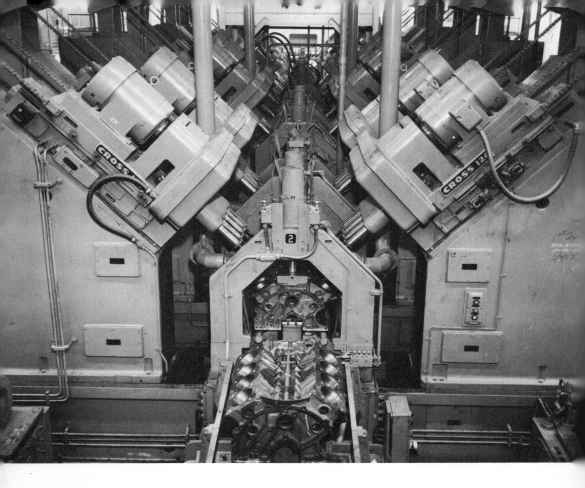

Giant machines drill and ream valve guide holes on engine blocks at the super-automated Lima Engine Plant. (Courtesy Ford Motor Company)

Pistons start as rough, shaggy forgings and emerge at the end of their line as gleaming units ready to install, with piston rings installed and in measured, balanced sets of six or eight. Even more amazing, these sets are already scheduled for installation in individual blocks already selected, but at that point far on the other side of the plant going through their own processes. This selection is done by interconnected quality-control machines, which also then assure that the proper set of pistons will reach the proper assembly point just as the proper cylinder block arrives there. Seldom has either been touched by man during their machining. Meanwhile, connecting-rod forgings are making their own trip down their manufacturing line and they, again premeasured to fit particular piston units, meet the pistons at the proper point. Joined together, they go to meet their private cylinder block among the thousands in the process of manufacture.

In another part of the plant, rocker arms are being ground and heat-treated, crankshafts are being milled, ground, and balanced, and camshafts are going through the same operations. All will meet at the proper point of assembly and, almost always, be machine mounted and machine tested. The entire process is a marvelous example of modern technology, and there is always a waiting line of visitors wanting to watch. Employees (and there are still thousands of them to keep watch over the machines) begin to seem like actors on a stage.

Perhaps most interesting and complex of all the operations, and certainly that which involves the heaviest single part of an engine, is along

Here a row of cylinder heads begin the long journey down the line, all by automation. (Courtesy Ford Motor Company)

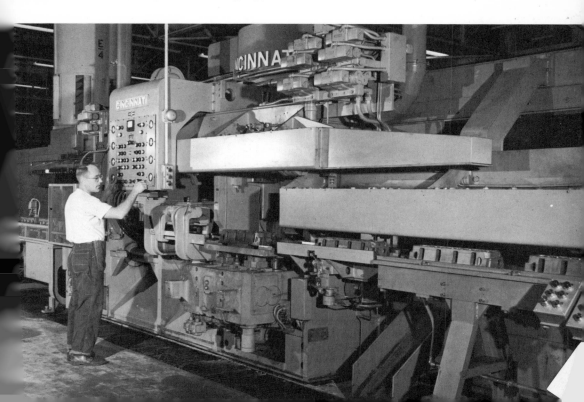

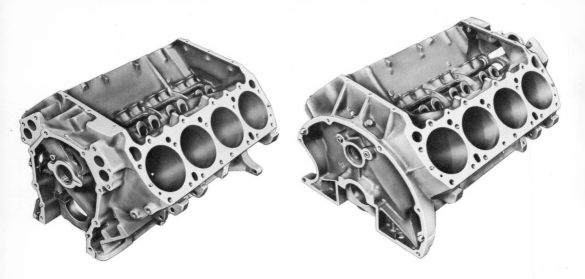

Finished cylinder blocks; front and rear views. (Courtesy Chrysler Corporation)

Finished piston and connecting-rod assembly. (Courtesy Chrysler Corporation)

Finished crankshaft. (Courtesy Chrysler Corporation)

the "block line." Here the cylinder blocks are turned from rough castings with sand still clinging to them to smooth, painted, polished engines. Several hundred pounds in weight, each block is drilled and surfaced and milled and honed automatically by machine. In several cases, one single machine does a large number of separate operations all at the same time, for much work is needed to complete this basic frame of the engine.

The cylinder block is the frame that contains and holds the cylinders in proper alignment. Since most automobile engines are water cooled, each cylinder and the entire upper part of the block is "jacketed" or double walled to allow for a flow of water around the hottest part of the engine. In most modern engines the cylinder block also includes the crankcase (in aircraft radial engines, for example, the cylinders are separate from the crankcase and bolted on during assembly), so that is also a part of this heavy cast-iron unit.

The cylinders themselves are like polished tubes inside the cylinder block. The pistons will travel up and down in these tubes, and the number and placement of these sleeves or tubes determines another part of the general classification of an internal-combustion engine.

The engine might be a standard in-line six-cylinder model, or a V-8, even a V-12 or V-16—or something else altogether. There are many different types of cylinder arrangements, depending upon the job the engine is to do. In the aircraft-engine section of this book, you will read about the above-mentioned radial engine.

But let us here stay with automobile engines and their cousins, the engines for trucks, tractors, and other wheeled vehicles. The standard passenger-car internal-combustion engine is normally either an in-line or a V-type, in-line being just what the name implies, with the cylinders lined up in a row. V-type engines, then, have their cylinders in a "V" formation, with equal numbers on each side of the V. An in-line-6 (or straight-6) would have six cylinders in a row. A V-8, such as the "Indy" racers now use, would have eight cylinders, four on each side in a V formation. A straight-8 would have eight cylinders in a row, and a V-12 would have six on each side.

Still another cylinder arrangement that has become popular recently on certain small, four-cylinder, compact cars is the "horizontally op-posed" engine. This arrangement has two cylinders on each side, directly opposite from each other.

So, back at the engine plant, the cylinders in the cylinder block are arranged and cast according to the type of engine being manufactured, and are open at both ends at first. This is so they can be easily machined and polished and made ready for installation of pistons.

Since there will be no high compression at the bottom end of the cylinder "bore," this end is left open inside the engine. In this opening, which is directly over the crankshaft and in which the connecting rod has room to move, there is no further work to be done. But at the upper end of each cylinder, or each bank of cylinders, a cylinder "head" is bolted in place to close the top of the engine.

This head is another casting that has been machined to a perfect smoothness to match the smoothness of the cylinder-block top. This fit must be tight and perfect, for high compressions will exist in this area of the engine—the upper part of each cylinder and the cylinder head (along with the top of the piston) forming the combustion chamber.

The cylinder head is also double walled, or jacketed, if the engine is to be water cooled, for high temperatures will exist here as well. A gasket,

Finished camshafts. (Chan Bush photo)

Finished rocker arms. (Chan Bush photo)

Finished exhaust manifold. (Courtesy Chrysler Corporation)

usually made of copper or copper-asbestos, is bolted between the block and the head. It forms the final seal between the two parts and prevents any escape of burning gases with the resulting loss of compression.

In fact, you have probably heard of a "blown head gasket." This means that the gasket between the head and the block has ruptured and is allowing compression to escape. This is not a serious matter, but still the gasket must be replaced before the engine will operate properly. The replacing job is actually rather interesting, and one which can be managed by the owner of the engine providing he follows simple instructions.

Of course, at the Lima Engine Plant all this is done by huge machines.

Once the head is fastened to the cylinder block (and with certain other attachments to seal the system) the entire cylinder section of the engine is surrounded by a water jacket. Temperatures inside the engine will vary from over 1,000 degrees to nearly 4,000 degrees, and if this water jacket with its cooling water flowing through were not there, parts inside the engine would simply melt. The water carries away much of this constantly developing heat, keeping internal temperatures within certain operating ranges.

This is the "cooling system" of the engine. The water circulating around the engine, driven by a water pump which is fastened to the front end of the crankshaft, passes through a "radiator" apart from the engine.

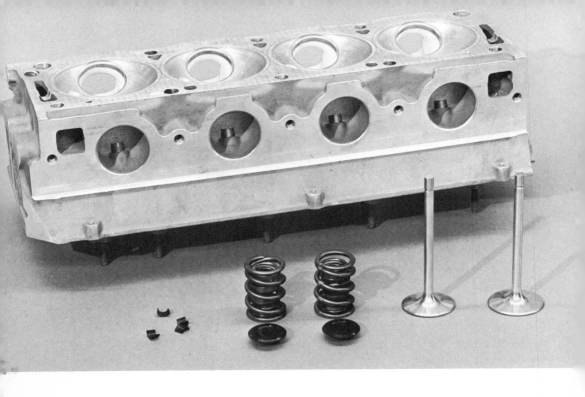

Finished cylinder head, with valves and valve springs shown for one cylinder. (Chan Bush photo)

View into the combustion chamber of the "hemi-head" engine. (Chan Bush Photo)

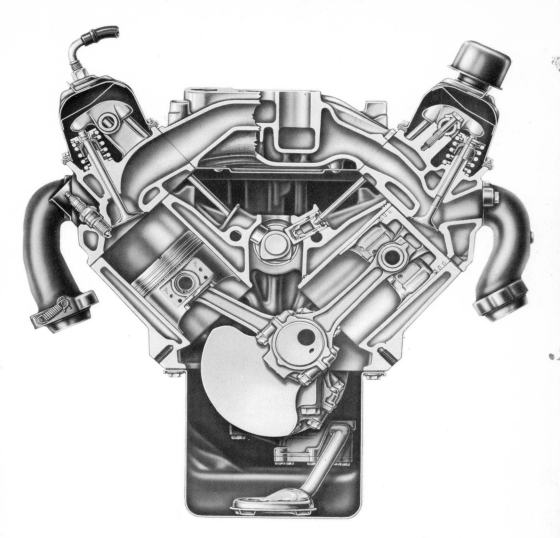

Cross-section view of a V-8 engine, with internal parts in position. (Courtesy Chrysler Corporation)

This radiator, with a fan drawing air through it, cools the water enough to be recirculated again and again through the water jacket around the engine. This action continually carries away heat, and the engine operates at the correct temperature. There is even a "clogging" device in this

47

closed water-circulating system known as a "thermostat." This thermostat can restrict the flow of water for if the water is allowed to flow freely it can cause the engine to run *too cool,* so efficient is the water-cooling system of a modern engine. The thermostat controls the flow of water, slowing the entire action, and allowing the water to hold at least a part of its heat as it goes back through the water jacket.

The crankcase is located at the bottom of the block where the cylinders stop. This, as the name implies, is the housing for the crankshaft. Here cooling is not needed, for the very high temperatures of the top of the engine will not come down this far. The crankshaft spins inside this crankcase as the pistons and rods drive down and up and down and up. The power of the engine is taken off at the ends of the crankshaft, projecting from each end of the engine.

You know what happens when you rub two of almost anything together—your hands, or a file on a piece of wood, or even two pieces of paper. Friction heat is generated, and in some cases very high, destructive temperatures can develop.

You can then imagine what would happen to the walls of the cylinders inside an engine, or to the piston rings, if the engine were allowed to run without some type of protection from friction heat. Almost immediately

The oil pump and pick-up head of a modern engine's lubrication system. (Chan Bush photo)

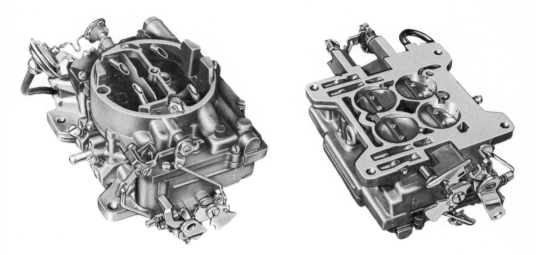

The modern four-barrel carburetor. (Courtesy Chrysler Corporation)

the walls would score and fail, or the rings would crumble or melt. This would happen only seconds after the engine was started.

So engine builders have devised ways of getting oil to the moving parts of an engine. This oil, under pressure from an oil pump located in the oil pan of the engine and driven by the action of the engine, is applied directly to every moving part inside the engine. Sometimes it is squirted through specially drilled holes, which direct the oil exactly where it is needed; sometimes it is splashed to where it is needed; and sometimes (around the upper rocker arms, and so on) it is allowed to flow where it is needed. Then all the oil runs back down into the pan to be picked up by the oil pump and once again forced into the areas where needed. The walls of the cylinders are continually coated with protective oil brought up from the pan by first the oil pump and then "oil rings" around the pistons. This coating of oil on the walls of the cylinders reduces the friction and allows the pistons to slide up and down smoothly.

Meanwhile, oil is being forced into the mechanisms that operate the valves, into the rod and crankshaft bearings, and into all the other areas of motion in the engine. If your engine is "burning oil," it indicates that oil is being carried up the walls of the cylinders and into the combustion

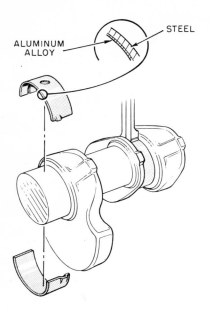

ALUMINUM ALLOY — STEEL

A view showing the method of mounting bearings on the main bearing surfaces of the crankshaft. (Courtesy Chrysler Corporation)

A view showing the method of mounting the spark plugs so that the electrodes project into the combustion chambers. (Courtesy Chrysler Corporation)

1966 — 1967

1966 POLYSPHERIC TYPE

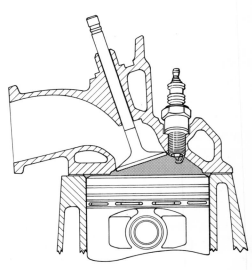

1967 WEDGE TYPE

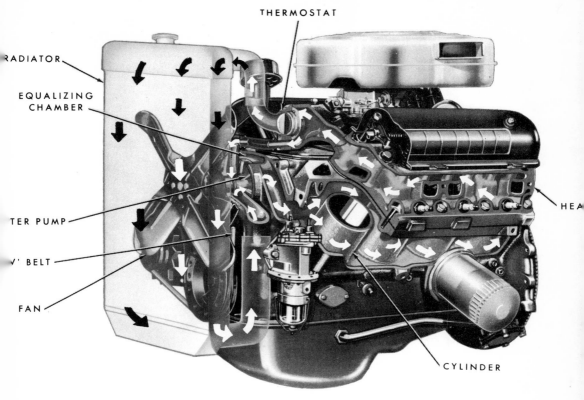

THERMOSTAT

RADIATOR

EQUALIZING
CHAMBER

TER PUMP

'V' BELT

FAN

HEA

CYLINDER

A drawing showing the cooling system of an engine. (Courtesy Ford Motor Company)

chamber where it is being burned with the incoming fuel. That is why an engine that is burning oil smokes—the burning fuel does not smoke to any degree. In the case of an engine burning oil, the compression rings may have started to fail and too much oil is being carried up the walls of the cylinder and above these rings.

The oil pump and lines form the "lubrication system" of the modern internal-combustion engine. The oil you add in the oil-inlet pipe, which projects up from the engine, runs down into the oil pan to mix with the oil already there. You merely bring the level up to the mark on the "dip stick," which is a measuring device placed in the engine for that purpose.

Incidentally, you need not worry about adding competitive brands of oil into the same engine, for modern government standards have been set which insist that all oils match and blend together smoothly.

So, when the service-station attendant says, "You're about a quart low, sir," he means that he has shoved the dip stick down into the engine's oil pan, checked the line on the stick, and found the oil level to be lower than normal by one quart in this case. The oil pan is bolted to the bottom of the crankcase, and forms the very bottom of the engine. It is made of pressed steel or aluminum, not cast iron, for it does not have to be nearly as strong as the other parts of the block, nor does it need to be cooled by circulating water (though in certain high-performance racing and aircraft engines, the oil is circulated through its own cooling radiator).

If the engine is air-cooled, which is the case with certain modern compact cars, no water jackets are needed. Such an engine is much lighter in weight than the water-cooled engine, even though it does have extra fins of metal around the cylinders and cylinder heads to allow for cooling as the air washes across it. Several very popular horizontally opposed four-cylinder engines in use today are air-cooled. Air cooling is also common in engines for small airplanes.

the "hot-test" line

At the engine-manufacturing plant, the overhead conveyor lines begin to come together near the shipping docks like the tracks at a railroad terminal. Here you suspect that an end product is being attained after all the apparent chaos throughout the plant. You are right, for hanging from these conveyors are gleaming, ready-to-run engines, all set to be shipped to an automobile assembly plant for installation in new cars.

Only one step remains, and that is to be sure the engine actually runs—for although it has been assembled with critical precision, it has never been started.

So, again automatically, each engine travels down a long "hot-test" line seeking an open dock into which it can come to rest. Switches click and the engines are lowered into place. Oil is added, water lines hooked up, fuel lines plugged into carburetors, and a starter is joined.

Almost invariably, with only one or two turns of the crankshaft, the engine rumbles into life. It is an exciting thing to watch these engines operate for the very first time, for inside them are thousands of brand-new parts that have never before been in action. Yet each part has been so carefully built and inspected and installed that only very seldom is trouble found. If trouble is found, the engine is then routed back to the area where the problem can be solved.

It is interesting to note just how all these parts work together to provide mechanical energy from heat energy of burning gases. You are familiar now with the cylinder block and head (or heads, in the case of V-type engines), but what about the operations inside the engine?

Let's examine a piston and its attachments. This is the tin-can-shaped device that moves up and down inside the cylinder. Usually made of forged aluminum, it is microscopically ground and polished to shape to fit the cylinder exactly, and in the case of an engine just being built, to fit the *individual* cylinder into which it will eventually be installed (for there are minor variations even in modern machining). Up inside the hollow piston is a "piston pin" that holds the upper end of the connecting rod in place. The pin "floats" in the piston, but is pressed into the rod, giving free action back and forth, but no action at all up and down. Any action up and down, any sloppiness in the fit of the pin in the rod or piston, would of course result in a great deal of noise inside the engine as the pin slapped about while the piston was streaking up and down. For a very short time, that is; then the entire unit would simply break apart. The rod, however, must move freely sideways in the piston in order to allow for its lower, larger end to move back and forth as the crankshaft spins.

So the piston glides up and down inside the cylinder, and from it projects a connecting rod that can move freely back and forth at the bottom, with its pivot point at the piston pin up inside the piston.

Around the piston top are mounted piston *rings* (in specially cut grooves called "ring lands"). The rings are snapped into the lands and then the unit is squeezed into the cylinders, after which the rings attempt to snap back out a bit. This gives an absolute seal between the piston and the cylinder wall, since any leakage here would cause lost compression and very poor operation. Usually two sealing rings, or "compression rings," and one "oil ring," a heavier, open-faced ring that carries oil up the wall of the cylinder for lubrication, are used. The oil ring is the lowest of the three, so that oil cannot be carried up into the combustion chamber above the upper two compression rings where it could burn away.

Pistons are precision-fitted and tight in the cylinders, but they are not so tight that they cannot be moved up and down by hand in an open cylinder, with the heads removed. Yet only the compression rings actually *touch* the cylinder walls at the top of the cylinder bore, in spite of

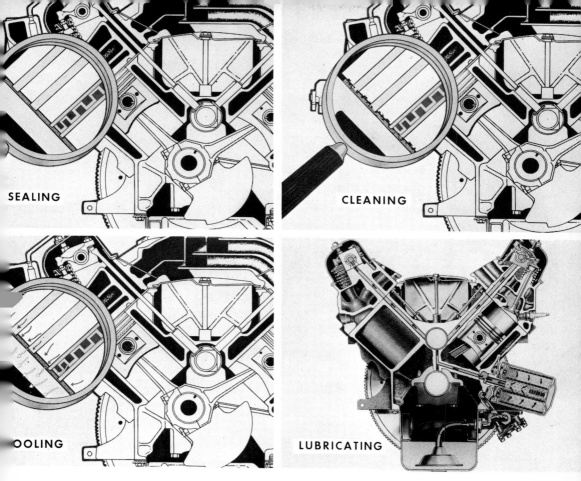

SEALING

CLEANING

OOLING

LUBRICATING

A diagram showing the lubrication system of a modern V-8 engine, and the different jobs of this system. (Courtesy Ford Motor Company)

the fact that the fit is so precise that you cannot possibly see the tiny space between the piston itself and the cylinder wall.

Inside the crankcase is the odd-looking device called the crankshaft. It does not look as though it would do anything, really, for it seems to be all off-center and bent and twisted, with heavy counterweights sticking out at random places. It is actually a high-precision piece of machinery, critically built and delicately balanced. If it were not, the engine would quickly fly apart.

A *racing* piston and connecting rod. (Chan Bush photo)

The crankshaft, basically, changes the up-and-down or reciprocating motion of the pistons into a turning, or rotary, motion. Each crankshaft has a certain number of cranks, or "throws," depending upon the number of cylinders (and thus pistons and rods) in the engine. If the engine is an in-line-six, then the crankshaft will have six throws, each with a smooth bearing surface to which the connecting rods are attached. The crankshaft also has other bearing surfaces where the main bearings, or "mains," are located. This is where the crankshaft is fastened to the engine crankcase. The crankshaft spins in its main bearings.

Each throw, or crank, is displaced at an angle to the others so that when the bottom ends of the connecting rods are attached, the pistons will be in their proper positions inside the cylinders. Then, when one piston is on its downward power stroke, the others are in some other position of operation, not in opposition to the first piston. It is logical not to have two or three pistons trying to make power strokes at the same instant, each working the crankshaft in a different rotary direction. Something would quickly have to give! So in a four-cylinder engine, for example, let us say that one piston is power-stroking the crankshaft around, another is exhausting gases due to an upward thrust of the rod and piston, another is drawing fresh fuel into its own cylinder, and the fourth is compressing its fuel for the next power stroke—which will follow instantly and keep the engine running.

And that is not all that must be considered in operating an engine. Camshafts, or a single camshaft in some engines, must open valves at exactly the right instant to allow for exhaust of used gases and intake of fresh fuel mixtures. These camshafts have a row of eccentric cams, two for each cylinder in the engine, that are geared or chained to the crankshaft so that the cam turns at one half the speed of the crank. As the eccentric cams (see illustration) spin, they operate against cam followers and, generally, push rods (depending upon the type of engine), to open the valves correctly. Since the cams are precisely ground and the camshaft geared to the operation of the engine, the unit works very efficiently. The camshaft (or camshafts) may be located in the head or heads of an overhead-cam (OHC) engine, or in the crankcase or in the bottom of the "V" of a V-type engine.

Racing engines often have four valves per cylinder to allow for a quicker expulsion of exhaust gas and quicker intake of unburned fuel, and in these cases we often see a double-overhead-cam engine (or four camshafts). The gearing in this engine, located under a cover at the front of the engine, is really very interesting, for it is quite complex.

The valves themselves are mushroom-shaped devices that merely open and close holes in the combustion chamber. Strong springs hold them in the closed position until the camshaft, often through a rocker-arm assembly, forces them open momentarily. Then, at the moment the peak of the eccentric cam on the camshaft passes, the valve snaps shut again. Naturally the valves must fit precisely, for no leakage can be tolerated around the valve "seats," where the valves rest in the combustion-chamber openings. Again, a loss of compression and poor operation would be the result of leaky valves.

You have often heard of "burned valves" or of a car "needing a valve job." Here, the valves have become damaged or burned and are allowing compression to escape. They must be replaced or reground, another interesting job that can be handled by the "Sunday afternoon mechanic" with a little textbook assistance and certain hand tools.

In motor-racing contests, in which engines are required to sustain high speeds for great lengths of time and in which they are often pushed beyond their design limit, an engine might "swallow a valve." This is racing talk for a valve breaking off inside the cylinder. You can imagine the instant result of this chunk of hard metal banging around inside the combustion chamber of an engine.

Goodbye engine!

The flywheel is a nonheroic but very important part of every engine. Placed at the rear end of the crankshaft, this carefully balanced heavy wheel spins at the speed of the crankshaft. This is the actual "power take-off" of the engine. The rapid spinning of the flywheel also stores up power during the power strokes of the pistons, then releases this power (keeping the engine turning) during the other strokes, thus helping the crankshaft to maintain a constant, smooth speed. The rim of the flywheel has teeth which are joined to a gear in the starter motor when starting the engine. In an airplane, the propeller acts as the flywheel for the engine.

The engine is all set and ready to run, but it still needs other items to get it going and to keep it going. One of these is the fuel system.

One end of the fuel system is very simple—a container for fuel, a gasoline tank. The other end, though, becomes quite a bit more complicated, especially in automobiles. The gasoline must pass through several devices and be altered considerably before it is finally burned in the combustion chamber of each cylinder.

First the gasoline generally passes through a fuel filter, located along the gasoline line from the tank. This filter will remove any remaining microscopic impurities that are still in the fuel in spite of the precautions taken by the oil companies and the service stations. Any bits and pieces, no matter how small, will scratch around inside the cylinder if they get that far, or might clog the tiny openings of the carburetor. One man, having trouble with his engine, watched as a mechanic finally tore the entire intake-manifold system off the engine in an effort to locate the

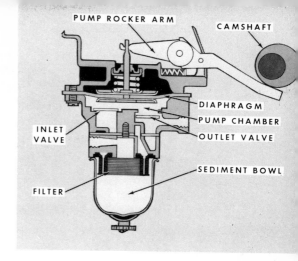

A self-explanatory drawing of the modern fuel pump. (Courtesy Ford Motor Company)

PUMP ROCKER ARM

CAMSHAFT

DIAPHRAGM

PUMP CHAMBER

INLET VALVE

OUTLET VALVE

SEDIMENT BOWL

FILTER

trouble. Everything appeared to be perfect. Finally, the third time the carburetor was disassembled, a tiny bit of matter was found which had been working in and out of one of the jets, causing the trouble. Twice before, the carburetor had been *boiled* to remove just this sort of thing, but the bit of clogging material had remained. You can see that the fuel filter is important (though often forgotten for the life of the engine) and should be changed regularly.

What makes the gasoline move in the system? A fuel pump, connected to and operated by the engine, pumps the fuel from the tank and forces it on into the next device, the carburetor.

This instrument (and it is just that) accepts the raw fuel from the fuel line and mixes it with a precise amount of air before allowing it to go on into the engine. Leaving the carburetor, the mixture (now a vapor) enters the "intake manifold," upon which the carburetor is located.

This intake manifold is a cast-iron, precisely machined device that directs the vaporous mixture coming from the carburetor to the intake-

A drawing of the intake manifold of a modern engine. (Courtesy Ford Motor Company)

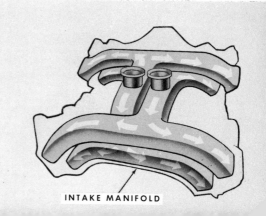

INTAKE MANIFOLD

valve ports in the combustion chambers. It is generally located on the side of an in-line engine, and in the valley between the cylinder banks of a V-type engine. It is little more than a series of passageways, but they must be just right for the engine to perform efficiently. Slight changes in the bends of these passageways have a great deal of influence on the operation of the engine; in fact, one simple method of "souping up" an engine is by smoothing these passages for better gasoline mixture flow.

Also a part of the fuel system of the internal-combustion engine is the "exhaust manifold" and the other pipes that carry burned fuel away from the engine. The exhaust manifold is an iron casting fastened to the engine over the exhaust-valve ports. Burned gases leaving the combustion chamber through the exhaust-valve ports are directed through the exhaust manifold and away. In a passenger automobile, truck, or most other highway vehicles, these gases then pass along a pipe, through a "muffler" to deaden the sound of the rapidly burning gases inside the engine, and then out the tail pipe.

But don't think for a minute that this can be a haphazard affair. If you do, just take a look at the tangled, twisted, "spaghetti" pipes carrying away the exhaust of a high-performance engine in, for example, a racing car. Certainly the standard passenger automobile exhaust system does not go into this very great detail, but the pipes are measured and balanced to at least some extent. In a racing-car engine, the exhaust is actually "tuned" by critical measuring and bending and cutting of pipes to carry away the exhaust gases. Builders calculate the conformation of the pipes so that an absolute minimum of back-pressure is encountered, actually so that each pipe helps every other pipe to carry out the gases by forming vacuums in the exhaust system *between individual ignitions of fuel in the chambers.*

Talk about precision! We cannot even come close to hearing the individual ignitions, and builders actually tune to them by bending pipes.

But all the same, if you for some reason added three or four extra bends in your exhaust pipe just for the fun of it, or just to look "racy," you would notice a difference in the performance of your engine.

So our internal-combustion engine has fuel, it has lubrication, it has

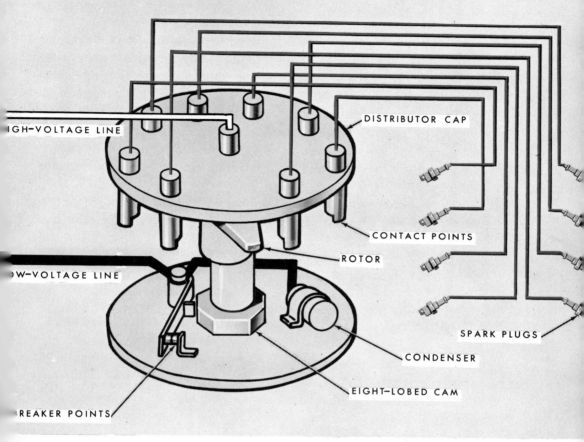

HIGH-VOLTAGE LINE

DISTRIBUTOR CAP

CONTACT POINTS

ROTOR

LOW-VOLTAGE LINE

SPARK PLUGS

CONDENSER

EIGHT-LOBED CAM

BREAKER POINTS

A diagram showing the ignition system of a modern V-8 internal-combustion engine. (Courtesy Ford Motor Company)

all the internal working parts to make it go as it should, and it has cooling water ready to flow around it. All it needs now is something to make it "combust," something to ignite the fuel we have provided.

This is done by the "ignition system."

This is the system of wires, switches, batteries, and other devices that all work together toward one single purpose—to make the spark plug "spark" at the right instant and ignite the compressed fuel in the combustion chamber of each cylinder. Let's take a look at the ignition system part by part.

Initial power is provided by a storage battery located near the engine. This battery does the double duty of providing electricity to turn the starting motor and current to spark the plugs. Once the engine is running, the system operates differently, but it must begin to run before it can continue running. So the starting motor, a simple little electric motor temporarily geared to the flywheel, turns the engine's crankshaft—but very slowly, of course, for the gearing must be such that the little electric motor can spin the big engine in spite of the effort required to overcome compression.

Meanwhile, current is flowing from the battery through an "induction coil," which steps up the voltage considerably since a high voltage is

A self-explanatory drawing of a modern V-8 engine. (Courtesy Chrysler Corporation)

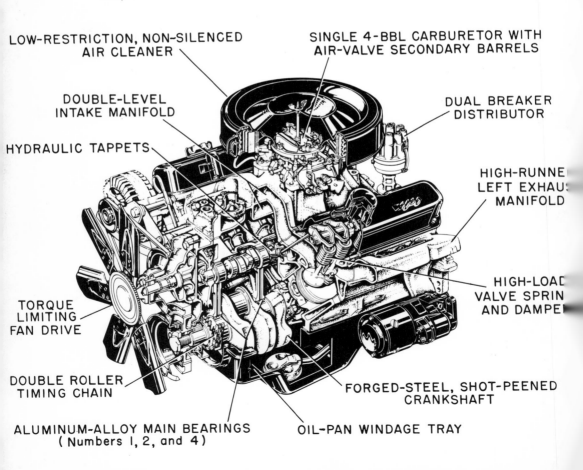

LOW-RESTRICTION, NON-SILENCED AIR CLEANER

SINGLE 4-BBL CARBURETOR WITH AIR-VALVE SECONDARY BARRELS

DOUBLE-LEVEL INTAKE MANIFOLD

DUAL BREAKER DISTRIBUTOR

HYDRAULIC TAPPETS

HIGH-RUNNE LEFT EXHAU MANIFOLD

TORQUE LIMITING FAN DRIVE

HIGH-LOAD VALVE SPRIN AND DAMPE

DOUBLE ROLLER TIMING CHAIN

FORGED-STEEL, SHOT-PEENED CRANKSHAFT

ALUMINUM-ALLOY MAIN BEARINGS (Numbers 1, 2, and 4)

OIL-PAN WINDAGE TRAY

required to make the spark jump across the electrodes of the spark plugs in the combustion chambers. The stepped-up voltage passes through a device known as a "distributor," which, just as its name implies, distributes the surge of high voltage to the proper spark plug at the proper time. It does this by means of a whirling "rotor" mounted on top of the spinning distributor shaft (geared to the camshaft) and connected by wire to the secondary winding of the coil. As the distributor shaft revolves, the rotor becomes a rotary switch and directs current to contact points embedded in the distributor cap, which covers the working insides of the unit. Each contact point is wired to a spark plug—with each cylinder in the engine having a spark plug, and each spark plug having a contact point in the distributor cap. As the turning rotor passes close to (but does not actually touch) the contact points in the cap, current flows to that particular spark plug. At the same moment, "breaker points," mounted on the same shaft as the rotor, open, and the surge of high-voltage current from the secondary (high-voltage) side of the coil momentarily flows. So the breaker points open and provide the high voltage, and the rotor arm sends this high voltage to the proper plug at the proper instant.

Then the points snap shut and low voltage once again flows in the system—but only for a brief instant. For almost instantly the rotor moves on to the next contact point, the breaker points snap open again, and another surge of high voltage from the coil flashes to a spark plug.

Since there are as many spark plugs as there are cylinders, and as many contact points as there are spark plugs, and as many point openings and closings as contact points, each plug gets a surge of current at the proper point, if the engine is "timed" correctly. Each spark plug is screwed directly into the cylinder wall or head with its electrodes projecting into the combustion chamber—so the actual spark occurs within the chamber itself.

Consider how precisely this whole operation must function. The distributor is really an astonishing little device. An eight-cylinder internal-combustion engine, operating at an average 4,000 revolutions per minute, must have *16,000* correctly delivered sparks *every minute*. That is about 12,500 sparks of 15,000 to 20,000 volts every single mile, or more than 250 sparks every second, or one spark every .004 second. For every thousand miles the breaker points in the eight-cylinder internal-combustion engine distributor open and close about *12,500, 000 times.*

So, instead of just imagining the engine turning over slowly, let's start it up.

One master switch is provided on an internal-combustion engine to activate the system, and this is in the form of a key or switch in the ignition system. It could almost as well have been somewhere in the fuel system, but this would neither shut off the engine instantly nor be as convenient, so the ignition system is the "on-off" system.

The key is switched on, providing a flow of current through the separate parts of the ignition system, then the starting motor is activated (usually from the same switch key). The engine turns over slowly at first but then, with only a couple of turns if all systems are functioning, the first spark occurs in a combustion chamber and the fuel ignites. The piston is driven downward in its cylinder, increasing the speed of the engine. Another spark plug flashes and more fuel is ignited. Then another and another as the pistons reach the proper positions in their individual cylinders.

Suddenly the engine is running. The starting motor disengages itself from the flywheel by the automatic action of a spring on its drive shaft, and the engine is on its own. But here a change takes place. With the engine turning over under its own power, with fuel flowing properly, and with all other systems functioning, a device known as a "voltage regulator" clicks inside and the electrical current flowing in the ignition system is rerouted.

The battery which was used for starting the engine no longer needs to provide current for the spark plugs, for a "generator" takes over. Driven by the engine itself, the generator not only provides current to spark the plugs, but also provides enough extra current to recharge the storage battery which started the engine, replacing the current used from it during starting. The generator also provides enough current to operate any accessory equipment located on or around the engine. On some engines

64

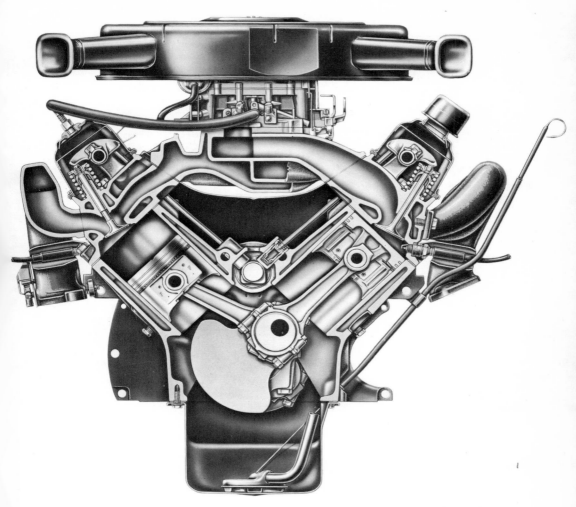

A cutaway of a modern high-performance V-8 engine showing location of internal parts. (Courtesy Chrysler Corporation)

an electric fuel pump is used, so the generator provides the current to operate this pump. Although they are not parts of the engine, the generator also has enough output to operate the horns, lights, and other accessory equipment of the automobile or truck in which the engine is mounted.

Many modern engines are mounted with an "alternator" in the place

A hot-rod engine, ready to run. (Chan Bush photo)

of the generator, but this is just a more efficient device to do the same job. The advantage of an alternator over a generator is that the former will provide more current at lower speeds, but both operate in basically the same way.

Inside the running engine, many operations are all working smoothly together to keep things going. The pistons are moving up and down in the cylinders, driven by the force of the expanding gases that are being ignited by the spark plugs and that are burning in the individual combustion chambers.

The camshaft or camshafts are popping valves open at the right instant to allow for the intake of fuel and the exhaust of burned gases. The crankshaft, driven by the connecting rods from the pistons, is spinning, and is making the flywheel also spin.

Oil is being circulated to friction areas inside the engine, and water is passing through the water jackets around the heated areas and carrying the heat to the radiator for cooling. The radiator fan, driven by a belt from a pulley on the crankshaft end, is pulling air through the radiator to cool the water for recirculation by the water pump.

This internal-combustion engine is an amazingly precise device when one realizes just how many separate actions and reactions must occur with split-second timing in order for the unit to operate properly. Yet they do function efficiently for hours at a time, for days and weeks and months if they are given proper care and maintenance and provided with fuel, lubrication, and cooling water. Thousands of these engines have driven automobiles many hundreds of thousands of miles without a mechanic's wrench touching them.

Trucks, airplanes, and boats travel the highways, airways, and waterways, all powered by these wonderful engines. The racers at Indianapolis speed up to over 200 miles per hour driven by internal-combustion engines, and some men have traveled far faster than this using the modern engine.

Driver Rodger Ward in his famous 1965 "Indy" racer. This is a high-performance Ford racing engine. Note the "spaghetti" exhaust system, explained in the text. (Indianapolis Motor Speedway photo)

Speedster Mickey Thompson, from California, built a car with *four* of these internal-combustion engines, one for *each wheel*. If one engine must work with great precision, imagine what it was like to get four of them to work together with split-second timing! Thompson did, and his car went over four hundred miles per hour on the famed Bonneville Salt Flats of Utah.

Of course at these speeds, and at any speed, every part of the engine must work properly to keep the entire complex running. A number of basic things can go wrong to keep the engine from starting or to make it operate poorly. We know, first of all, that the engine must have fuel, and it must have electricity. Without both of these items, no engine will run—so if an engine will not start, these are the first two things mechanics look for.

Perhaps the engine is running, but not smoothly.

Again, several things can be at fault. The electricity may be there, but perhaps it is not reaching the spark plugs at the right instant. If it is not, the engine is said to be "out of time." Chances are the distributor has failed in some way, and is either not sending the current regularly, or is sending it at the wrong times. This is not a serious matter as a general rule, for the engine can be "timed" by almost any amateur mechanic with a timing light.

Perhaps the plugs are not firing properly. Another simple matter. They can be cleaned, regapped (the electrodes must be a precise distance from each other), or even completely replaced for only a few dollars. And anyone can do it, too.

Fuel may not be reaching the combustion chambers in the proper amount or at the proper time or in the proper mixture. Too much fuel and the engine will not run properly, but too little fuel will bring the same result. In these cases it could be the fuel pump failing to bring the fuel to the carburetor, or the carburetor failing to mix it properly, or something as simple as that speck of dirt lodged in the fuel line or carburetor.

If an engine is running rough or erratically, the valves could be at fault. Perhaps they are not "seating" correctly, and are allowing a loss of

Another high-performance racing engine, here shown with the "king" of all drag-racing drivers, Don Garlits. (Chan Bush photo)

The same type engine in action! (Chan Bush photo)

compression. This can be corrected, as mentioned before, by either grinding the valves and valve seats, or replacing the valves.

Engine manufacturers build modern internal-combustion engines to operate for years and years, but they also build them to allow for reasonably uncomplicated repairs in case something does go wrong. It is even possible to repair an engine that has suffered a connecting-rod failure, with the result that the rod snaps under high speed and punches a hole right through the side of the engine (and this does happen). Fortunately, this is a rare occurrence, generally happening only when the engine is not given proper maintenance, or when it is operated beyond its design limits.

To prove that statement, here are some interesting facts about the American passanger car, the prime user of internal-combustion engines. Car life, and thus engine life, has *doubled* since 1925, when the average engine lasted about six and a half years. Today the average is more than twelve years. In 1925 the average engine drove a car about 25,000 miles before it needed major repairs or an overhaul, while today the average is over 100,000 miles.

Today the average distance traveled by a passenger car is 10,000 miles per year. Automobiles zip along in great numbers on roads across the country, at high speeds on modern turnpikes, superhighways, and freeways. This is a far cry from the Red Flag Law in England in 1865. That country's lawmakers actually passed a law requiring that someone walk or trot ahead of every automobile, waving a red flag to warn people in the area. There were similar laws in the United States, some designed to protect the sensitivity of horses. In Vermont in 1894, for example, there was a law to the effect that no one could drive a car on a public highway unless someone walked ahead to warn the occupants of oncoming carriages.

Today, in the United States, there are now *twenty* motor vehicles for every single mile of road and street. That is an amazing number of operating internal-combustion engines.

Where did they all come from? Where did it all start?

development from 1820 to 1914

The meeting was being conducted by the Cambridge Philosophical Society in England, and scheduled to speak was the Reverend W. Cecil. The year was 1820.

Cecil was finally introduced and he approached the rostrum with a sheaf of papers in his hand. There was a stirring in the audience of intellectual scientists and students, for Cecil was known to be an "experimenter" with odd and unusual devices. As he began his speech, silence settled, but it was not completely a silence of respect and attention. Many in the audience rebelled at the words of the speaker as he read from his papers, and a few violently disbelieved what he was saying. His ideas were difficult to comprehend, to say the least.

He was reading a paper he had prepared listing certain experiments he had conducted with a so-called "internal-combustion engine." He described it confidently, explaining in detail that he had used an up-and-down piston arrangement, with the energy to drive this piston being provided by burning a combination of hydrogen and air. Burning the mixture above the piston, according to Cecil, caused an expansion of gases in a small space, and this expansion drove the piston downward. It was similar to a steam engine in operation, insisted Cecil, but with the power stroke coming from energy created *inside* the engine itself.

It was an astonishing idea, and many of the assembled listeners refused to believe that such a thing was possible. Yet this early, basic idea of Cecil's is believed to be the very first working internal-combustion engine in history.

In a one-room brick workshop, Henry Ford built this motor car in 1896, which led to the immense Ford empire. Powered by a two-cylinder engine, it had no reverse gear but a forward speed of nearly ten miles per hour. It was tiller-steered and weighed about 500 pounds. (Courtesy Ford Motor Company)

There is a law of physics, a basic truth, that energy can neither be created nor destroyed—that nothing, in fact, can be created or destroyed. Things can be *changed*, but that is all. A log placed in a fire and burned is not destroyed, but only changed into another form. Indeed, in its "creation" as the limb of a tree, it was only changed into that limb from the earth and the sun and the rain, from elements that were already there. Everything here now has always been here, and always will be here in our universe. The modern clothes you wear were here in prehistoric times, in a different form. The energy that drives our rockets to the moon was available to the cave men, and so were all the materials necessary to build the rocket. The automobile we drive was here, and could have been built thousands of years ago, if materials were all that was needed—for even the fine steels and rubbers and plastics and glass and copper wiring were available, though in a somewhat different, unrefined form.

Only *knowledge* was lacking. It has taken us thousands of years to learn how to do the things we do, so the availability of energy and materials really does not matter. Without question, we have all around us today materials to put together new forms of energy and new devices that would stun the mind, which some of us might even automatically reject and repel as being impossible or inconceivable. We would react probably just as the cave man would have feared and rejected the halting experiments of the Greek inventor Hero of Alexandria—and he is so ancient that we cannot even pinpoint the *century* in which he lived and worked. He, incidentally, built a number of devices that were powered by steam, using them for such purposes as opening temple doors.

Throughout the ages of man, fire was tamed into heat and light for caves, and coal was discovered. Man learned to harness water for grinding grain, to force the wind to turn work-saving windmills, to use magnetism for compasses, and to use explosive forces such as sulfur and naphtha to kill his neighbor.

Believe it or not, man was "accomplishing" this latter "science" as early as A.D. 670, for that is when we believe a Syrian alchemist called Callinicus invented the first incendiary bomb.

Steam power was known to the ancient Greeks, but it was fifteen more centuries before man really developed its potential. An English military engineer named Thomas Savery patented a device in 1698 which he called a "steam engine." It was an inefficient, but ingenious, device. In fact, the word "engine" originally meant *any* ingenious device, and came from the same Greek root as "ingenious."

Savery's engine could be used to pump water out of a mine shaft or well or to turn a water wheel. But it was finally James Watt, who had been called in to repair one of the early models of steam engine, who made the device really work. He studied the engine he was to repair. It had been built by English blacksmith Thomas Newcomen and had, for the first time, a piston that moved inside a cylinder. Watt improved the engine, greatly increasing the efficiency with new mechanical ideas and linkages, and this became the first real working steam engine.

Meanwhile, electricity was being studied by such men as the French chemist Charles Francis de Cisternay du Fay who discovered that two glass rods, electrified by brisk rubbing, would repel each other. The same was true with two amber rods. Yet he found that a glass rod and an amber rod would attract each other, and if allowed to touch, would lose their electricity. This led him to believe that there were two different kinds of electricity, "vitreous" and "resinous."

Benjamin Franklin, who was lucky to have lived through some of his very dangerous kiteflying experiments, continued the studies and discovered negatively and positively charged materials. All of this, and far more of course, led to the making of electric motors and storage batteries.

So we had basic elements and gases, we had a knowledge of heat energy, we had the "prime mover" (a thing that takes energy already existing and turns it directly into work) of steam, and we had electricity. We knew of pistons and vacuums and we already had steamships traveling across the Atlantic Ocean on regular routes (by the 1830s, in fact, with screws rather than side paddles). We even had a steam-driven "horseless carriage" built by William Murdock in 1786 (a century before the famed Stanley Steamer, built by Francis Edgar Stanley in 1886).

But we did not, in spite of all this knowledge and all these somewhat similar devices, have a workable *internal*-combustion engine. There seemed to be one major drawback to the development of this type of engine. Although certain ones had been built and operated by such men as Cecil in 1820, and others somewhat later, they all used fuels other than gasoline. These fuels were inconvenient, difficult to obtain, and difficult to store.

Another English inventor, William Barnett, patented a *gas* engine in 1838 which actually compressed the fuel mixture—gas, not gasoline, and so still very inconvenient. Barnett's engine was a single-cylinder unit with a piston that traveled up and down, compressing and igniting fuel at both ends.

Finally, in 1860, French inventor Jean Joseph Étienne Lenoir built the first really practical internal-combustion engine. His engine used street-lighting gas for fuel and a storage battery for electricity. It has an electric ignition system, though this idea was not yet widely accepted. By 1865, Lenoir was manufacturing his engine in numbers, with over four hundred of them being used in Paris for such jobs as powering printing presses, lathes, and water pumps. During this time, Lenoir also built a vehicle and mounted his engine into it, but it did not work well.

Beau de Rochas, another Frenchman, worked out a four-stroke-cycle engine on paper in 1862, then he moved on to other projects. Working with de Rochas' ideas, a German technician named Nikolaus August Otto finally constructed a true four-stroke-cycle internal-combustion engine that worked. He did this in the year 1866 and by 1876 he and

Karl Kizer of the Speedway Museum shows the odd valve and rocker-arm arrangement of the 1914 Eddie Rickenbacker Duesenberg race car. (Indianapolis Motor Speedway photo)

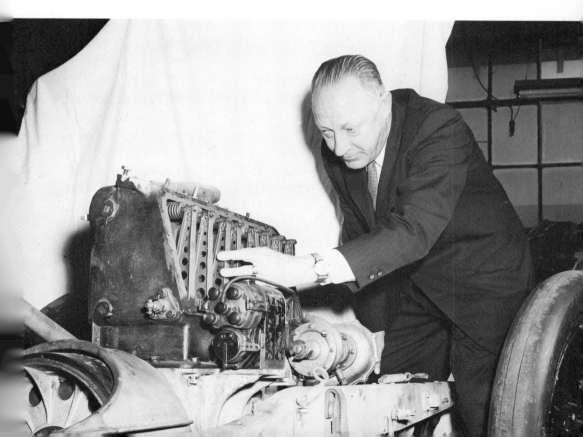

Eugen Langen, another German, applied for and received United States patents on both two-stroke-cycle and four-stroke-cycle engines.

Then came one of the important steps forward in the development of the internal-combustion engine as we know it today, yet it was a most logical step. Until then, inventors had been working on one-cyclinder engines. A Scottish engineer named Dugald Clark studied the engines that had been built, and a great idea came to him. If one cylinder worked as well as it did, then why not two? He hooked up a second cylinder, so that its piston was compressing fuel while the first was on its power stroke. This increased the power output of the engine, and made it run much smoother and steadier too. It was named a "reciprocating" engine.

Still, the trend was to the Lenoir-type, gas-powered, two-stroke-cycle engine, and in Austria in 1864 a man by the name of Siegfried Marcus was finally able to devise a way to use a *gasoline*-air mixture for fuel. This brought the principle of the internal-combustion engine close to what we have today, but still in a very primitive form of course. Marcus even built a crude vehicle for his engine, but, like Lenoir's, it was far from satisfactory. In 1876, in competition with the Otto and the Langen engines, an American by the name of George B. Brayton built and exhibited a gasoline-powered engine. Otto's and Langen's patents covered *gas*-powered engines, you will recall.

Finally, an associate of Otto and Langen designed and built the world's first successful four-stroke-cycle, gasoline-powered internal-combustion engine. His name was Gottlieb Daimler, who became famous as an automobile-building tycoon. Daimler built his engine in 1885, and tested it the same year in a strange vehicle with his son as the driver. It was probably one of the most comical (and certainly one of the most important) rides in all the history of engines, for it brought about the modern internal-combustion-engine equipped automobile.

It was, indeed, an unusual engine to say the very least. Consider the "spark plug" it used. To supply heat for ignition, Daimler resorted to a most basic form—a *Bunsen burner*.

Daimler's engine had a long, skinny, upright single cylinder that was gasoline-fed through a very basic carburetor. As the fuel mixture, which

Leon Duray's winning 1929 racer and engine. (Indianapolis Motor Speedway photo)

Daimler called the "explosive vapor," was introduced to the cylinder, a bit of it drifted over to the Bunsen burner, where it ignited. This ignited the remainder, of course, and the piston was driven downward. (In many of the early-day internal-combustion engines, in fact, the combustion chamber was not only in the top of the cylinder, but also beneath the entire top cover of the engine. Often the valves were located several inches away from the cylinder, and so combustion occurred everywhere from the valves to the cylinder top, and down inside.)

For this historic occasion, the first time an internal-combustion engine was to "successfully" drive a manned vehicle, Daimler built an odd combination of pipes and wooden frameworks. Over the top, reminiscent of a horse, he threw a leather saddle, and up front, projecting between the driver's legs, he had an ungainly looking tiller. The entire vehicle was unsprung, making for what would obviously be a rugged ride over the cobblestone streets of Cannstatt, Germany, the home of the inventor.

So Paul Daimler, Gottlieb's son, lighted the Bunsen burner with confidence. His father's other inventions had worked as he said they would, so why not this one? Next he turned the huge crank that projected from the side of the engine's crankcase. To the amazement of the by-standers, who had come to get a chuckle out of old Gottlieb's machine, the engine popped twice, banged, and started.

Until then, nobody had really thought that an internal-combustion engine could be made small enough, and light enough, to power its own weight plus the weight of a vehicle and a man driving. For one thing, these engines had always had a remote supply of fuel from tanks mounted elsewhere, not from a small tank mounted directly upon the vehicle itself. Spectators pressed forward with interest, for it appeared that the first major hurdle had been cleared. The engine was actually running, and it did not sound bad at all.

Still, the major idea was to propel a vehicle, not merely to run an engine with a vehicle-mounted fuel tank. Obviously this odd-looking little engine of Daimler's would never do that.

Carefully mounting, with a side glance at his calm father for some

Jules Goux, a famous race-car driver, and his winning 1913 racer. (Firestone Tire & Rubber Company photo)

reassurance, Paul pushed the control rod that at the same moment released the rear brake and engaged an idler pulley to apply tension to the drive belt around a pulley on the rim of the rear wheel. The machine lurched forward. Stepping down hard on two side-mounted footboards, Paul tripped a lever that retracted the "landing gears"—these being a kiddy-type "helper" wheel on each side to help maintain the balance of the vehicle.

On two twenty-six-inch iron-clad wheels, Paul clanked and sparked merrily away, and the wobbling "motorcycle" picked up speed. Soon he was outrunning pedestrians who had been strolling alongside grinning foolishly but still amazed at the performance. The huffing, puffing, smoking engine, turning at a then-astounding speed of 700 revolutions per minute, chugged on and Paul realized that he was traveling at a breakneck *seven miles per hour!*

But not for long. A sloping hill loomed ahead, and gradually the bike slowed . . . and slowed . . . and s-l-o-w-e-d. . . .

The pedestrians, who had managed to keep up with Paul Daimler's careening speed, jumped to assist. Falling in behind, they pushed and once again the engine speed increased. Paul had not even had to lower his landing gears. The hill was topped, and Paul continued down the other side.

But not too fast, for old Gottlieb had also devised an ingenious governor on his engine. The faster the engine ran, the less fuel would enter the combustion chamber, due to the action of a valve Daimler had mounted beforehand. So the speed of the vehicle stabilized, and as the crowd cheered in the background, Paul Daimler charged away on his first historic ride.

And it was historic, for the vehicle proved for the first time that an internal-combustion engine could be mounted in a vehicle, and could then propel that vehicle forward, carrying along at the same time a fuel supply and a man. The engine could be made powerful enough, and yet small enough, to do all this.

The Germans were well ahead of other nations in the development of the internal-combustion engine, for at about this same time a German by

An old (1909) Indian motorcycle on display at the Speedway Museum. (Indianapolis Motor Speedway photo)

the name of Karl Benz was perfecting his own engine and engine-driven vehicle. He had started much earlier with his original designs, of course, and by 1878 he had produced a working internal-combustion engine. He designed and built his first motorized vehicle in 1885, the same year as Daimler's first run, but Daimler preceded him by a short time. Benz's vehicle, however, had developments of higher sophistication, items that are still in use today in much improved forms. His engine boasted an electric ignition (no Bunsen burner) and it was water-cooled. His vehicle had a differential gearbox to change the direction of the power train, and to divide it between the rear wheels of his three-wheeled machine.

He also devised a float-type carburetor and a transmission system, both of which we still use today in improved forms.

Bentz's machine looked very much like a three-wheeled carriage without the horse, and it was steered by a tiller that projected up in front; but still it was another of the primary forerunners of modern-day automobiles.

So Gottlieb Daimler formed the Mercedes Motor Car Company and Karl Benz formed Benz and Company (in Mannehim, Germany), manufacturer of motor cars. Eventually the two merged into the Mercedes-Benz Company of modern fame.

A Frenchman, Émile Levassor, was responsible for locating the internal-combustion engine at the front of vehicles, as is the general practice today. He and René Panhard, partners in a carriage-building firm in France in the 1890s, decided to go into the manufacturing and selling of motor vehicles, using Daimler's engines. Levassor decided to mount the engine in front, rather than in the rear, and to make the machine look like something other than a horseless carriage. He devised a means of transmitting the power to the rear wheels by a gearbox and chain.

Finally, men in the United States began to design internal-combustion engines for vehicles. Charles E. and J. Frank Duryea built the first successful gasoline-powered automobile in this country in Springfield, Massachusetts, in 1893. It was the major attraction of the Barnum and Bailey Circus for the next few years, outdrawing even the daredevil trapeze artists. People flocked to watch the Duryea machine being driven around the center ring, probably never imagining the astounding future of the machine they were cheering.

The Duryeas were quickly followed by Elwood G. Hayes, who designed what he considered to be an even better engine-vehicle combination. Hayes turned to Elmer and Edgar Apperson and Jonathan Dixon Maxwell to build his car for him. And famous names that still shine brightly in the history of American engine and auto production begin to appear. For these four men, Hayes, the Appersons, and Maxwell—and of course the Duryeas—became famous for auto production. Their grand

Engine output per cubic inch has been multiplied fifteen times between the Model T engine on the left and the modern Ford engine on the right. (Courtesy Ford Motor Company)

old motor cars are still in collections, many in running condition, proudly carrying these names on ornate hood emblems.

Of course the engines, and indeed the vehicles themselves, are somewhat comical and so basic in design and construction that one wonders how they ever operated at all, but they are still fine old machines and very interesting to study. A few antique-lovers even claim that these original, simple internal-combustion engines were more reliable than the complex ones we have today; but this is certainly open for argument.

A banner year for the production of motorized vehicles was 1896. Using designs of their own, and borrowing ideas from previous builders, came Charles Brady King, then the fabulous Henry Ford (who revolutionized the entire industry with production line and "mass production") and then Alexander Winton and Ransom Eli Olds, who had earlier built steam carriages but recognized the trend to motors.

Of course, we still have Ford automobiles, and Ford engine plants, and Oldsmobiles. The Winton, while it lasted, was a fine machine.

Automobiles powered by efficient internal-combustion engines became commonplace transportation, finally pushing the horse aside. Only one thing was left for man to do with his new machine, and that was to fight with it. Sure enough, World War I came along and, though the automobile had until then had very limited use in warfare, an incident occurred that changed the entire picture.

In September, 1914, the Germans were threatening Paris with occupation. General Joseph Gallieni, the military governor of the city, commandeered every single taxicab in town to rush his troops to the front, and the German Army was driven back in the Battle of the Marne. The "taxicab army" of Gallieni had changed the course of the war, and in a short time an endless stream of motor vehicles was in use to rush troops where they were most needed. Some of these vehicles were armed and armored, leading eventually to such war machines as tanks.

workings of cylinders

Until Scotsman Dugald Clark came along, early-day internal-combustion engines were one-cylinder units of very low power and efficiency. They worked, but just barely. The slightest extra force exerted against their torque (their power output at the crankshaft, basically) would stop them. A few could be stopped by hand. They were "low-compression" engines with thin walls and long, skinny pistons and connecting rods.

But then Clark thought of putting two cylinders side by side, and the idea worked. The first "in-line" engine was a reality. Still very low in power, but far better than the single cylinder, the trend became obvious. Perhaps someone next tried three cylinders, but this would not have worked nearly as well, for the engine probably would have seemed out of balance with three pistons working.

So four were tried, and once again power increased and engine operation became more efficient. Since then, in-line engines always have an even number of cylinders—two, four, six, eight, twelve, or even sixteen.

For many years the in-line-4 was the standard, then the in-line-6. These, as previously discussed, are engines with either four or six pistons working to common crankshafts. The shaft in the four has four cranks, and in the six has six cranks. In the in-line eight-cylinder engine, or "straight-8", the crankshaft has eight cranks connected to the eight pistons by connecting rods.

By 1932, the dean of all engine manufacturers in the United States, Henry Ford, had built his company into an empire. At first he had gone along with the others, building cars that were very expensive, so only very rich people could afford them. Up to about 1913 it took workers several days to assemble an engine and then a complete car, even though parts were ready and waiting. Henry Ford examined this method of building, and at the same time decided that every American should be able to afford a motor car. He streamlined his assembly processes by opening "assembly lines." A bare frame of a car would pass down a line before workers, and each worker would add something to the slowly but constantly moving frame. The time to assemble a complete car, engine and all, dropped to only 93 minutes except for the body—and the body was added in a few more minutes just outside the plant. Using these methods, Ford workers turned out over *fifteen million* cars of one particular model from 1908 (before mass production) to 1927, when the model was finally changed.

They were very popular, and people who had never before owned an automobile were able to own one of these, for Ford finally polished production techniques enough to be able to bring the price of this model, ready-to-run, to only $290. Of course they were all exactly alike, all black, and all with the very same accessories, but they became a legend in the United States. Today, many men still recall them fondly.

"There was a car you could trust," they say. *"There* was a car you could fix if something went wrong. All you needed was a little grease and a little bailing wire."

No matter your age, you will recognize the name of this grand old engine and car that became an American institution. It was the famed "Tin Lizzie," the incredible Ford "Model T."

But finally the Model T gave way to an improved version known as the Model A, and in the meantime other manufacturers of engines and cars were giving Ford stiff competition with their own products. Oldsmobile was a popular car, if you could afford one, and Maxwell (which later became the giant Chrysler Corporation) was also a best seller. Buick and Cadillac and Studebaker cars appeared in increasing numbers, as did Chevrolet and Oakland (later Pontiac) and the famous old Stanley Steamer. And there were more, each with its own factory-designed and factory-built internal-combustion engine.

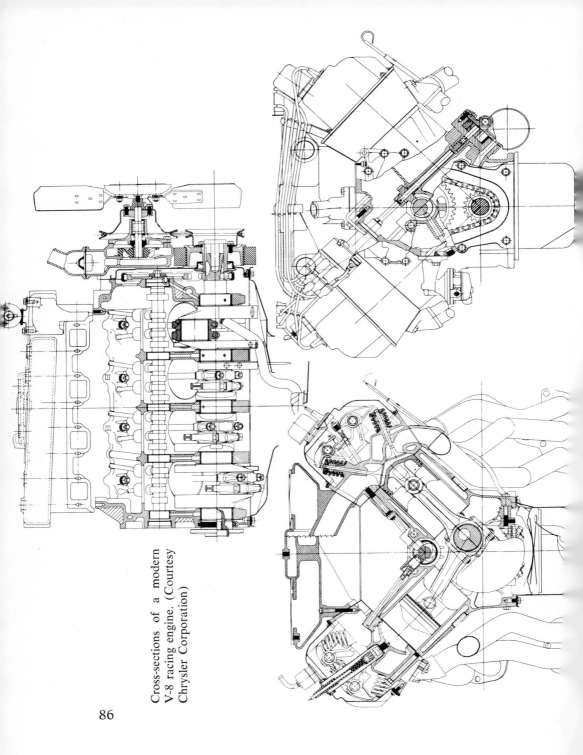

Cross-sections of a modern V-8 racing engine. (Courtesy Chrysler Corporation)

Dodge, Pierce-Arrow, Stutz, and Duesenberg attracted a segment of the auto-buying public. Overland (later Willys) and Hudson and Packard were popular with others. Rambler (later Nash—and now we have a Rambler again) and Lincoln were popular.

Still, with general differences that each company claimed made its own product better, each engine was basically the same (except for the electric- or steam-powered models, of course). Each car had an engine that varied only in size and accessories to every other car's engine. The automobile had been doing fine, the industry had found a good thing in the in-line design, and they were staying with it. It was a reliable engine, and it was certainly fast enough for the roads of the day.

So, by 1932, Ford was king—but he was still dreaming and still inventing. His company was a giant in the industry, but he was still sitting at his desk doodling figures on scratch paper—for first of all Henry Ford was an inventor, and second the president of a huge company. He loved inventing more than anything else.

Upon his paper one day appeared a new, strange engine shape. The cylinders were side by side rather than in a row. They were angled away from each other slightly so that the connecting rods from the pistons met at a common point below in the crankcase. The drawing appeared to be two separate four-cylinder engines joined together at the crankshaft.

Ford built the engine and it worked far better than even he had dared hope. In a shorter space, a far more compact unit was actually running much smoother than anything had before, and it was still putting out more power than ever before.

The engine received the name "V-8" due to its odd new cylinder alignment. It was an overnight sensation. Automobile buyers loved it, and quickly other manufacturers designed and built their own V-8-style engines. Others built V-4 or V-12 engines, and one even build a monster V-16. The V-8, though, became the most popular engine in the world. It worked exactly as the others before it had worked, being a standard four-stroke-cycle engine, but the method of firing from the opposite sides of the crankshaft brought about a silky smoothness of operation, and made for a much more compact unit.

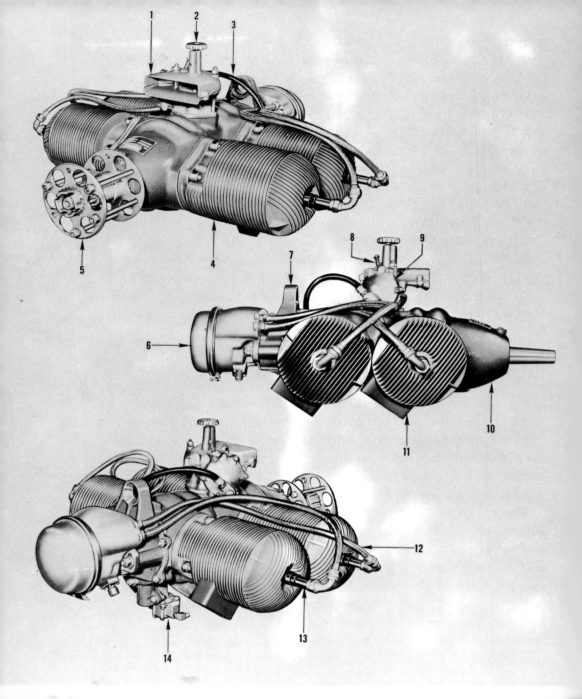

1. Carburetor	4. Cylinder	8. Primer Plunger	12. Ignition Harness
2. Needle Valve	5. Propeller Hub	9. Fuel Inlet Housing	13. Spark Plug
3. Fuel Line	6. Magneto	10. Crankcase	14. Fuel Pump
	7. Engine Mounting Flange	11. Exhaust Port	

This engine had eight pistons and connecting rods, but only *four* cranks on the crankshaft. To each crank was attached *two* connecting rods.

This is still the most popular engine today, and is the one used on most of the Indianapolis racing cars. In this case, however, the engine used is

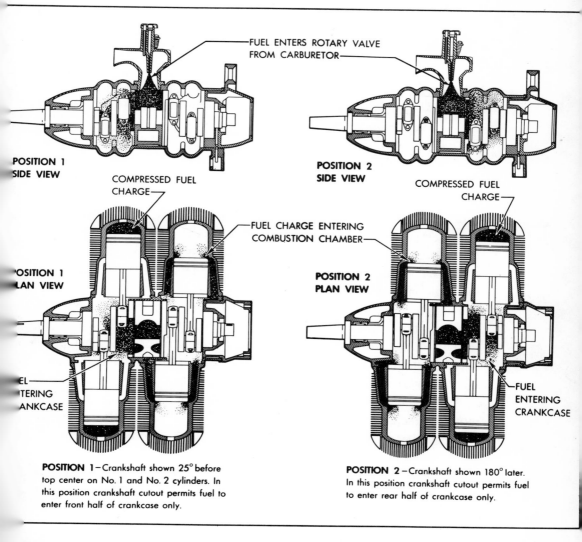

FUEL ENTERS ROTARY VALVE
FROM CARBURETOR

POSITION 1
SIDE VIEW

COMPRESSED FUEL
CHARGE

POSITION 2
SIDE VIEW

COMPRESSED FUEL
CHARGE

POSITION 1
PLAN VIEW

FUEL CHARGE ENTERING
COMBUSTION CHAMBER

POSITION 2
PLAN VIEW

FUEL
ENTERING
CRANKCASE

FUEL
ENTERING
CRANKCASE

POSITION 1—Crankshaft shown 25° before top center on No. 1 and No. 2 cylinders. In this position crankshaft cutout permits fuel to enter front half of crankcase only.

POSITION 2—Crankshaft shown 180° later. In this position crankshaft cutout permits fuel to enter rear half of crankcase only.

Two self-explanatory drawings of the horizontally opposed style of internal-combustion engine. (Courtesy McCulloch Corporation)

really a high-bred cousin of the standard V-8, with double-overhead camshafts, special metal alloys, and other modifications and improvements (some of which will no doubt one day appear in standard engines). For example, the standard V-8 has two camshafts, each one operating both the intake and the exhaust valves on a single head, but the racing engine has a separate cam for intake and another for exhaust, *two* on each head. Still, the idea is the same—the efficient opening of valves.

But even with the V-8, the end had not been reached in engine design. Not by a long shot! Today we have the "horizontally opposed" type of internal-combustion engine, in which the cylinders are folded outward until they are exactly opposite each other rather than in a "V" shape. This is a very popular design on certain compact cars today.

There is also the radial-type internal-combustion engine; but more about this one in the next chapter.

One of the oldest, and now one of the newest, types of internal-combustion engines is the "free piston." Remember old William Barnett's experiments back in 1838? His gas engine was a form of free-piston engine, with ignition occurring at both ends of the piston stroke. But it was nothing like a modern-day free-piston engine, in which efficiency has been so much improved that designers of these engines claim they will one day replace all the others.

Today's free-piston engines, still true internal-combustion engines, operate on an entirely different principle, generating hot gases which are then used to turn turbine wheels. They will burn nearly any type of liquid fuel, including kerosene, peanut oil, or inflammable perfume. Here's how they work.

As a general rule these engines have one or more pairs of pistons mounted facing each other in a cylinder. Between them is the combustion chamber. Neither piston is connected to any type of rod or crankshaft, but rather floats freely inside the cylinder.

Fuel is introduced between the two pistons and then ignited, creating rapidly expanding gases. Each piston is driven to an opposite end of the closed cylinder, where they build a tightly compressed air cushion. During this action, the pistons are also compressing air in a chamber around the cylinder (just as though we had drilled holes in the cylinder walls of a standard engine, and were forcing air into the water jackets). This air is then directed back into the combustion chamber to force the hot gases into the blades of a turbine wheel. Meanwhile, the pistons are bouncing off the tightly compressed air in the sealed ends of the cylinder, and back toward the center again.

Reaching the center at the same instant, they have compressed and heated the air between them so hot that the new fuel, when it is admitted, burns and starts the cycle over again. There is a constant flow of superheated, highly compressed air flowing over the blades of the wheel from the cylinder of the free-piston engine. The turbine wheel is affixed to a shaft which goes to the work you wish to perform.

In 1967, at Indianapolis, there were thirty-three cars qualified to race, as is the custom. Thirty-two of them were equipped with high-performance internal-combustion engines like those we know—similar to the V-8 in the standard passenger car. The thirty-third car also had an internal-combustion engine, but it was totally different from the others. In fact, it was called "the engine of the future."

Though other race-car engine builders laughed when it first appeared on the grid, it soon proved that it could provide an exceptionally smooth form of power. It was fast enough and yet it idled as smoothly as anything a driver might desire. It gave almost instant acceleration, yet it seemed to provide ready power at any speed. At the start of the race, the car with the strange engine was in sixth position in the line-up. The green starting flag snapped down.

Incredibly, the car shot around all five of those in front, and by the time the racers were on the backstretch of the very first lap, the car was pulling rapidly away from the snarling field behind. And, whereas the others were roaring and howling, this one was moving almost silently. (Some men called it the "Swooshmobile.") So the race went, with the battle throughout being for *second* place, for the strange car was far ahead on almost every lap. Only when forced into the pits for fuel did the car drop back, but promptly upon re-entering the race it would once

Dressed and undressed, here's Parnelli Jones's famous 1967 Indianapolis turbine, the "Swooshmobile." (Courtesy Vince Granatelli)

again pull into the lead. The car was far ahead on the 197th lap of the 200-lap race when, to the great disappointment of the screaming fans, a small bearing failed in the machine's transmission, and the car dropped back to place in sixth position. But the future had been shown, for the racer had totally dominated the race, and at the end its unusual internal-combustion engine was still running perfectly.

Yet the engine was smaller, lighter, and cheaper than any other engine in the race, and it burned far less expensive fuel. What was it?

It was driver Parnelli Jones's famed gas-turbine engine. Owner Andy Granatelli had installed the standard little aircraft engine, an almost off-the-shelf model, into the sleek four-wheel-drive race car, and revolutionized auto racing—and perhaps highway driving as well. Until then, few people had even heard of a gas-turbine engine, and certainly most of them had not been familiar with it. Since then, millions have been wondering about it—and about when we might have such an engine in our own cars.

The turbine is almost as simple in operation as the old-fashioned mill wheel, for the idea is exactly the same. But rather than water, highly compressed gases turn the wheel of the engine. The turbine engine has three main parts, as opposed to many, many parts in a regular piston-type internal-combustion engine. The gas turbine has (1) a compressor, (2) a combustion chamber, and (3) one or more turbine wheels.

The compressor is a huge fan, which draws air into the engine and squeezes it into a small space. This compressed air is mixed with fuel and then burns in the combustion chamber, rapidly expanding to an even greater pressure. This high-pressure gas is then guided over the blades of the turbine wheels (just more fans), turning them at very high speeds. The hot exhaust gases then pass out of the engine through an exhaust manifold. The turbine wheels are connected to a shaft that goes directly to the work load, in the case of Parnelli Jones's engine, to the racing-car's transmission.

Even though the car did not win the race with its unusual engine, it certainly turned the minds of engineers to this type of equipment for future passenger cars. Very likely we will begin to see them on the

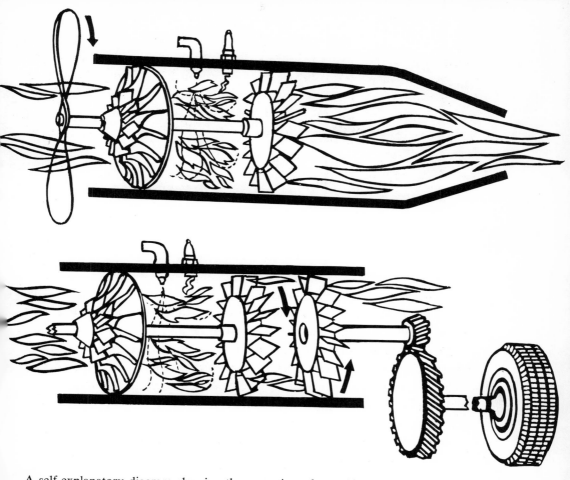

A self-explanatory diagram showing the operation of a turbine, both aircraft and automobile. (Courtesy Chrysler Corporation)

market before long (and one company, Chrysler, had a test model of a slightly different type on the highway even before Jones's drive). Certainly we will see more of them on race tracks as development continues.

Every engine must have a method of allowing fuel to get to the right place at the right time. We are most familiar with the carburetor method, for this is what is used on most passenger cars, buses, and trucks. This is the device that takes the raw gasoline from the fuel pump and mixes it with air to form a vapor which is then sent to the combustion chambers.

The engine of Jones's turbine. (Courtesy Vince Granatelli)

Carburetors are highly complex pieces of equipment, with many, many small parts and a number of critical adjustments. Inside is a float chamber which stores a small amount of fuel and also shuts off the flow of fuel to the carburetor when enough has entered. Inside are throttle and choke valves and tiny needle valves and openings. On top is an air cleaner. The entire unit is mounted, as we have learned, on the intake manifold which directs the fuel-air mixture to the cylinders.

This works well and is for the most part nearly trouble-free. Once a carburetor is properly adjusted, it will work for many thousands of hours with only an occasional cleaning or minor readjustment.

But engine men are always seeking something better. Something that will work more efficiently, or will make an internal-combustion engine more powerful or faster or more reliable. They knew that in the standard-engine fuel system, the fuel-air mixture is drawn into the combustion chambers by the action of the piston. When the piston traveled in the cylinder a partial vacuum was created, and when the intake valve opened the fuel mixture rushed in to fill this vacuum.

Yet the more gasoline and air that can be crammed into the combustion chamber, the greater will be the resulting power.

So "supercharging" was conceived.

Engineers invented a device that would *drive* the fuel-air mixture into

Drag-racing driver Tony Nancy with his racer. Note the huge "bug catcher" air scoop on the supercharger atop the engine. Here the air is picked up and then rammed into the engine. (Nancy photo)

With the result, here on driver Tom McEwen's car, that the front end rises up and smoke shoots from the spinning rear tires. (Courtesy Tom McEwen)

And with this possible result, which seriously injured this driver as the car went completely out of control. (Chan Bush photo)

the engine by means of fans. They could force a far greater amount of fuel into the engine than the mere action of a vacuum by forcing much greater volumes of air into the carburetor. This rapidly moving, highly compressed air picks up its fuel load and then *crams* it into the combustion chambers. Unfortunately this supercharged mass of air and fuel occasionally blows apart the engine, but the idea is sound if the adjustments are precisely made.

Many racing cars are supercharged, and so are many airplanes. In fact, quite a number of "standard" passenger cars have engines with supercharging equipment. But some of the most obvious of all the supercharged internal-combustion engines are those used by the exciting AA/ Fuel Dragsters now running on drag strips across the country. These metal framework "bombs" with a little cockpit out behind are unbelievably quick, with engines built to do one thing.

They must scream away from a standing start and cover one quarter mile in the fastest possible time. Huge superchargers sit atop these engines and when they rev up to start, the sound is an ear-splitting, thunderous scream. The power built into these engines, and about to be

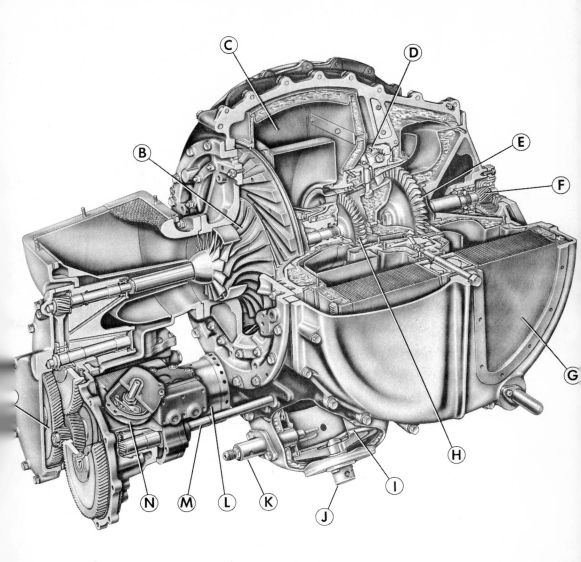

Cutaway drawing of Chrysler's twin-regenerator gas-turbine engine, showing main components: (A) accessory drive; (B) compressor; (C) right regenerator rotor; (D) variable nozzle unit; (E) power turbine; (F) reduction gear; (G) left regenerator rotor; (H) gas generator turbine; (I) burner; (J) fuel nozzle; (K) igniter; (L) starter-generator; (M) regenerator drive shaft; (N) ignition unit. (Courtesy Chrysler Corporation)

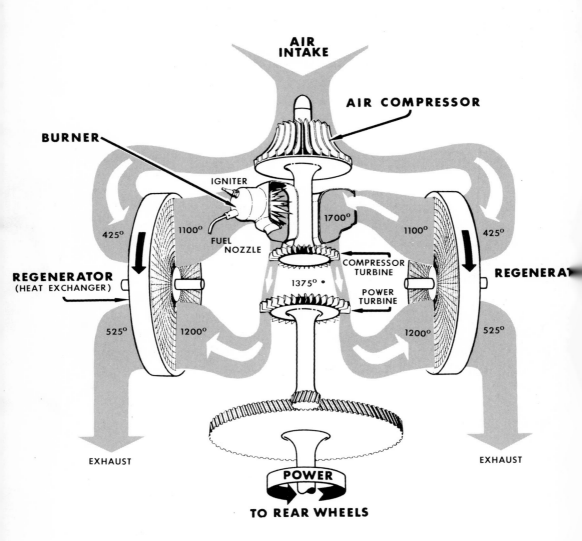

Diagram of the operation of a twin-regenerator gas-turbine engine. Note that the "regenerators" are heat-exchangers and cool the hot exhaust by using the heat in the incoming side of the engine.

unleashed, is almost unimaginable. Once standard auto or marine engines, they have been modified extensively. Their compression has been increased to the very limit, where one more ounce of pressure would shatter the engine—and often does!

Every single internal part has been strengthened or completely rebuilt to take the great strain of such operation. Every moving part has been braced and rebraced to keep it from bending or breaking. Then, to make the matter even more difficult for the engine, drivers use extremely powerful fuels rather than normal high-octane gasoline. A mixture of 20 per cent alcohol and 80 per cent *nitromethane* is not unusual. This may be terrible for mileage but it is just fine for great power.

When these revamped internal-combustion engines blast away from the starting line, the power is so great that the entire front end of the racer leaps into the air, and for many feet the huge rear tires boil smoke out behind as they attempt to get a grip on the raceway. For an engine lover, it is a painful and yet beautiful thing to see, and for everybody it is an exciting form of competition.

They are supercharged, and they are also "injected" with fuel. In this "fuel-injection" method of sending fuel to the combustion chambers, no carburetor at all is used. And this is not only for competition cars, for several standard sports cars are equipped with fuel injection—since there are advantages other than speed alone. Here's how fuel injection works.

It is nothing more than a system of "squirting" raw fuel into the cylinders of an engine by forcing the fuel under high pressure through nozzles at each cylinder. Diesel engines are injected in a similar manner but still not exactly the same. In the gasoline-powered internal-combustion engine the fuel is squirted into an intake chamber near each cylinder. Here the fuel mixes with air before it passes through an intake valve and into the actual combustion area.

Just like carburetion? Not exactly, for fuel injection overcomes certain disadvantages found in a carburetor. A carburetor mixes air and fuel and then the heat from the engine vaporizes this mixture to allow for proper burning.

But the expansion of the heated air as it passes through the intake manifold of a carbureted engine actually reduces the amount of air (relative to the amount of fuel) reaching the combustion chambers, and the individual cylinders receive different amounts of the heated fuel-air mixture depending upon their distance from the carburetor. In a carbureted engine, some of the fuel-air mixture often fails to burn because of improper vaporization, and so the engine may "flood" (get too much raw gasoline and fail to start or fail to run smoothly), or it may allow for a formation of ice in the carburetor in the winter, or it may "vapor lock" (overheat and form bubbles in the fuel line preventing the proper flow of fuel) in the summer.

With fuel injection, the engine's cylinders get only the amount of fuel that will burn in the amount of air that enters, and each gets an equal amount, with the nozzles breaking the fuel into a very fine spray so that it will burn completely. The cylinders get more air, since the air is not heated before entering, increasing the engine's power and efficiency. Cold engines that are fuel injected will start quickly and run smoothly. Squirting raw gasoline into the carburetor intake of a small internal-combustion engine to get it started, or to keep in going until it warms up, is simple fuel injection.

Since the throttle in a fuel-injected system controls only the *air flow* into the cylinders, the engine cannot be flooded.

Supercharging and fuel injection are modern methods devised to gain even more power and efficiency from the internal-combustion engine. At the same time, new alloys are continually being developed for use in the parts of the modern engine. Aluminum is a favorite metal of engine builders for use in pistons, for example, while connecting rods, which must be thin and yet very strong, are forged from blends of steel. The cylinder heads, blocks, and crankcases of modern internal-combustion engines are usually of specially formulated cast irons. The crankshaft itself, which must be very strong, is often an alloy of fine steels.

Still, every piston-type internal-combustion engine works basically the same, from little "one lungers" all the way to huge powerplants—and nearly the same as the ones first invented.

Chemical energy in gasoline, which is obtained from petroleum, is converted to mechanical energy by burning in the engine.

To do this, a fuel pump sends the gasoline from the storage tank to the carburetor (or the fuel injectors). The fuel is mixed in correct proportions with air and then passes into a chamber or chambers known as the intake manifold. Valves are opened at the proper time and the fuel enters a combustion chamber or chambers. A spark is created inside each chamber, igniting the fuel and causing it to expand rapidly. This expansion pushes on the piston, the only thing inside the chamber that can move.

The pistons push connecting rods that are attached to a crankshaft, turning the latter and providing mechanical energy in place of the previously existing heat energy. Since the cylinders in an engine fire individually, one at a time in their proper order, there is a constant new flow of mechanical energy being developed to turn the crankshaft smoothly.

In the eight-cylinder engine, specifically, one piston is power-stroking while the other seven are in various stages of recovery from their own power stroke. As the one finishes, another fires and strokes, and then another and another. Soon the cycle is back to the first one again, which has in the meantime exhausted the gases from the previous burning and brought new fuel into the cylinder to burn.

It is really a series of one-cylinder engines all working smoothly together.

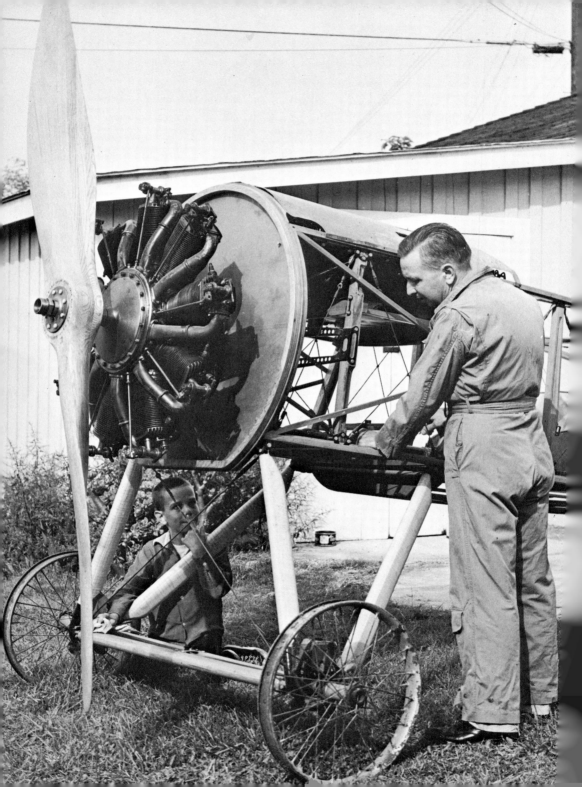

aircraft development

Immediately before and after the beginning of the twentieth century, a wonderful array of new ideas and inventions were placed in the hands of men. It was a golden age of inventions.

Man was suddenly able to send his voice great distances along a wire. He could also record his voice on a wax cylinder, and then play it back later. With no idea of just how great he was changing his entire future, he saw such things as the electric light, motion pictures, and the automobile powered by efficient internal-combustion engines.

He reacted to these wonderful things with varying degrees of interest.

One of the most astounding inventions in all the history of man, coming during those same few years, was almost totally ignored. It was an invention that would change the course of history and would affect the life of every single human in some way, most of them directly. It would change peacetime living, and it would have a violent effect on warfare. It would shrink the world, and eventually outer space as well.

Yet this outstanding invention was mentioned in only three newspapers when it was first tested and displayed. It probably was not that the newsmen were uninterested, but rather that they just did not believe

American Airlines pilot, antique collector, and rebuilder Ernie Freeman and his son Roger work on his Thomas-Morse Scout. This engine is one of the rotating radial engines that developed torque enough to twist the airframe and even cause the pilot to lose control. The engine is a LeRhone. (Chan Bush photo) what had happened. Only those who had seen it reported it. Others refused to pass the story on, for it was certainly one of the most unbelievable events in history.

This event occurred in the year 1903.

Two men who made a business of repairing bicycles in a small repair shop in Dayton, Ohio, began to experiment with gliders. It was a fascinating hobby, but they soon tired of little hand-tossed models and decided to experiment with man-carrying vehicles. Between 1900 and 1901 they built several such gliders and tested them at a location which has since become a familiar name in the history of the United States.

This location offered steady winds and the high sand dunes favorable to gliding, even though the gliders of the two men never left the ground. Undaunted, sure of their basic theories, they would return to their shop, study and improve their gliders, and return again to the sand dunes. Finally, in 1902, after constructing a wind tunnel and calibrating the actual affects of wind on the wings of a glider, they built a glider that flew. And so over one thousand glider flights were made and witnessed by the birds and a few spectators at Kitty Hawk, North Carolina, as the two men, the brothers Wilbur and Orville Wright, increased their knowledge of flying.

Returning to their shop again, they started work on their next machine. This one was to be different than the others. This one was to be larger, with a wing span of forty and one half feet. Working in secrecy (for surely they would have been ridiculed), they were also designing and building an internal-combustion engine. It was a four-stroke-cycle, four-cylinder, twelve-horsepower model with a bicycle sprocket at the power take-off of the crankshaft. Chains around the sprocket led to two wooden, pusher-type propellers in the wooden and piano-wire framework they called their "flying machine."

On December 14, 1903, the brothers took their machine to Kitty Hawk and assembled it, then flipped a coin to see who would be the first to "fly" it. Wilbur won the toss, but something went wrong and the plane would not leave the ground. So, after some adjustments and repairs, on December 17, Orville crawled into the framework, laid down on his

Jimmy Doolittle (front seat, wearing headset) tries a modern rigid-rotor helicopter. Inset shows Doolittle with a fixed-radial 1934 Lockheed Orion monoplane. (Lockheed-California photo)

stomach in the middle of the lower wing of the biplane, and Wilbur cranked the engine. It started.

Glancing to the right and to the left, Orville increased the speed of the two swishing propellers and the airplane inched forward on its wheeled truck. Faster it went, then faster still, with Wilbur helping it along by pushing.

And the machine left the ground!

Twelve seconds later, after a flight of 120 feet (modern airplanes have greater wing spans than this) the machine once again settled back on the ground—but the amazing deed had been done. An engine had been built with enough power and reliability that, placed into a winged framework, it would lift not only itself and the framework into the air, but a pilot as well.

But nobody believed it. The press almost ignored the historic flight, reporting it in only three newspapers. By the next morning the entire event was forgotten. A few people laughed at the "hoax" with which the three papers had tried to fool the public, for everybody knew that you couldn't make a heavy machine fly into the air. That was, they believed, a basic law of physics.

The Wrights, however, continued to improve their engine and airplane, and in 1905 managed a flight of 24.2 miles, proving that the Age of Flight was here. Still, even the government refused to believe that such a thing was possible. Government officials considered the Wright brothers to be "crackpots."

It took President Theodore Roosevelt, and the interest of several foreign nations (who were accepting the Wright's claims with a good deal more faith), to finally convince the government that airplane flying was important. Orville was finally allowed to show the airplane to a group of officials at Fort Myer, Virginia, in 1908 and when he took off, circled the field, and landed, the observers were astounded. A few reporters actually had tears in their eyes when they rushed to congratulate the grinning Orville Wright.

Unfortunately, with such progress there are always dangers, and a short time later an Army observer named Lt. Thomas E. Selfridge flew with Orville on a demonstration ride. A propeller snapped, shearing a tail wire, and the plane plunged to the ground. Orville Wright was seriously injured and Lt. Selfridge was killed, becoming the first man in history to be fatally injured in an airplane crash. There is now an Air Force Base named after him.

In spite of the fatal crash, the engine and airframe developed by the Wright brothers had been proven over and over again. Although far more slowly than might have been expected, the flying machine became a part of every man's life—even if it was a "circus" device for many years.

Aircraft internal-combustion engines developed from the Wrights' original model (which could just as easily have been used to power an automobile or a mine-shaft pump or a blower) into supersophisticated precision instruments now designed to do specific jobs in specific aircraft. There are engines of all sizes and shapes and styles, and engines that produce from as little as 100 horsepower to giants that produce many hundreds of horsepower. Yet, in gasoline-powered internal-combustion airplane engines, there are still two specific groups into which every single one can be classified.

In this composite photo, the same pilot (American's Ernie Freeman) is flying both the radial-engined Cessna Airmaster, which is taxiing, and the Astrojet overhead. (Chan Bush photo)

Modern aircraft engines of the reciprocating type will be either AIR-cooled or LIQUID-cooled. Small ones and large ones will fall into one or the other of these classifications.

Even with the blast of "prop wash" flowing back over the engine in an airplane, the smooth cylinder walls of a standard engine do not have nearly enough area to allow the heat to radiate away. Hot spots at the top of cylinders would quickly develop, eventually ruining the engine by melting parts. Engineers realized that more metal area around the cylinders and cylinder heads would make for more room for the heat from inside, and more surface area from which the heat could be blown away, or radiated away. So they placed "fins" around these areas, making an air-cooled engine easily recognizable. The fins only increase the surface area where the engine is the hottest, and the heat from combustion flows into this greater surface area to be carried away by the winds from the propeller.

A liquid-cooled engine in an airplane is very similar to the standard automobile engine, with a water jacket surrounding the block and head. The water, or fluid combination, is heated by combustion, flows through a radiator (which is cooled by the prop blast and the inflowing of air from the motion of the plane), then back around the block and head again.

Otherwise, aircraft internal-combustion engines work in the same way as automobile engines, with the same methods of providing power. Pistons compress a fuel mixture which is ignited, pushing the piston in its cylinder and turning a crankshaft. The crankshaft spins the propeller rather than the gears of a transmission in an automobile.

Small "private" airplanes generally have no more than four- or six-cylinder engines and usually develop only about 100 horsepower. Quite often they are of the horizontally opposed cylinder configuration, with two or three pistons on each side of the flattened engine. Air-cooled (you can see the fins), they are a dependable and long-lasting power source—even though they are watched far more carefully than any auto engine and are built with stronger parts inside.

Regular inspections and periodic tear-downs for rebuilding are required by such agencies as the Federal Aeronautics Administration, since an airplane engine must of necessity be more reliable than any automobile engine. There is no simple matter of pulling over to the curb in the event of engine failure in an airplane. Since these engines must be designed and built to be as light in weight as possible, and yet as dependable as possible, these inspections and tear-downs assure the pilot that his engine will always be reliable and ready for safe flight.

There is still another reason for the regular inspection of airplane engines. How often do you drive your automobile at *full throttle?* Very seldom, if ever, of course. Yet airplane engines are quite often required to operate at full power—on take-off, for example. So, once again, they must be inspected regularly to catch potential failures in parts or accessories before they fail in flight.

From these little engines in small airplanes the line goes up and up to huge engines of great power which, installed in airplanes in sets of two or four or even six, drive the giant airliners and bombers we have all seen in flight. But even these great powerplants will still fall into the general air-cooled or water-cooled classifications. Whether in-line or V-type they will still also work generally the same as an automobile engine in the same group.

One of the most striking and easily identified of all the airplane engines is neither in-line or V-type. This air-cooled engine is used exclusively in aircraft. It is a very interesting engine with an unusual cylinder arrangement and an odd connecting-rod and crankshaft design. A very popular aircraft engine until the advent of the turbojet, it was used to power a multitude of airplanes, among them the very famous "workhorse" of the United States Air Force, the *C-47* cargo airplane. It also powered the famous "Flying Fortress," the *B-17,* and the even larger *B-29.* The list could go on and on, for this fine engine is the very dependable and powerful "fixed-radial" type. The cylinders of this engine project out like the spokes of a wheel. It is still an internal-combustion engine but with little similarity to any other type in design or appearance.

Many years ago the standard aircraft radial engine was an odd device with a "torque" that actually twisted the body of the plane in flight,

A four-cylinder horizontally opposed target and drone engine for use on radio-controlled airplanes. Note dual ignition system. (Courtesy McCulloch Corporation).

occasionally causing the pilot to lose control and crash. In this early model, the cylinders were not fixed, but actually moved with the propeller around the central shaft. This spinning of the engine, combined with the spinning of the propeller, set up a force that was difficult to overcome. Some old-time fighter planes used this rotating radial engine, and a few still in the possession of antique-airplane collectors continue to be flown—but *very* carefully.

From the spinning wheel of the old radial engine finally came the safer and more efficient "fixed-radial" engine. In this one the cylinders are stationary, unmoving, and the engine works by forcing pistons to turn a crankshaft (and the propeller). Any odd number of cylinders may be mounted into the radial position, but the standard is usually seven or nine in the large engines mentioned above. Often engine builders mounted two radial engines front-to-back, doubling the number of cylinders that radiate from a common crankshaft—and this became the standard for military aircraft from such builders as Curtiss-Wright and Pratt & Whitney. These huge, heavy, double-banked-cylinder models had tremendous power and were almost absolutely dependable, many of them still flying home after chunks of flak had torn huge holes in them. The combat record of planes with these radial engines may never be equaled.

One of the unusual features of this type of engine is the connecting-rod arrangement, for the crankshaft of a radial engine has, of course, only one single crank (since the cylinders all radiate from a common point around the crankshaft). You will recall that V-type or horizontally opposed engines have a crank on the crankshaft for each pair of cylinders, and in-line models have a crank for each cylinder.

Naturally there is a connecting rod and piston for each cylinder of the radial engine, but one of these rods is called a "master" rod, and the others "articulated" rods. The master rod fastens to the crankshaft throw (crank) and the articulated rods fasten to the master rod. It works as though one man were turning a crank handle, with several other men helping by grasping the wrist of the first man. The engine is built in this way since there would not be room to mount each rod individually on the single crank. Forces are exerted in the same way as with any other engine, but the hook-up is different.

In each finned head, atop each finned cylinder of the air-cooled radial aircraft engine are "overhead" valves. The spinning crankshaft turns cams located in the front part of the engine. These cams force push-rods up, and these rods open the valves at the right instant to allow fuel to enter and exhaust to escape. Springs snap the valves shut the instant the pressure on the push-rod is relaxed (as the cam lobe on the cam continues its eccentric spin). Each cylinder on the radial engine is provided with two separate spark plugs. Indeed, there are two entirely separate ignition systems, which is called a "dual-ignition" system. Twin plugs in each cylinder, twin magnetos (which provide electrical current in the place of a heavy storage battery or generator), and two entire sets of wiring. It pays to be careful with an aircraft engine, and this dual system is an important safety device.

There is another major difference between a standard automobile internal-combustion engine and an aircraft internal-combustion engine.

Bearing in mind that an airplane quite often flies in a very erratic pattern, even upside down, can you imagine what this difference is? Let's look at the lubrication system.

In an automobile engine, you provide lubrication by adding oil to the oil sump at the bottom of the engine. You do this by just pouring in the oil. It lies at the bottom of the engine in the oil pan until it is drawn up by the oil pump and sent to wherever it is needed. This would not work in an airplane engine for if the airplane turned upside down then so would the engine—and all the oil would run "up" into the cylinders and cause the engine to fail. In fact, if you were to pour oil into a cylinder and then run the engine, the oil would take up so much of the space in the combustion chamber, increasing the compression so much, that very likely the extra pressures would bend or break the rods or pistons.

Then too, in a radial engine specifically, some of the cylinders are always upside down. So, rather than being in an oil sump as in the automobile engine, the oil in an aircraft engine is stored in a tank and pumped through tubes to the moving parts. Some of this oil is burned along with the gasoline, and some of it is recovered and pumped back to the oil-storage tank to be used again. While in the engine, the oil be-

An American Airlines Convair over Washington, D.C. This is the civilian version of the famed Air Force C-47, and uses twin radial engines. (American Airlines photo)

comes quite hot, so while on its way back to the oil-storage tank it is cooled by passing it through a radiator similar to the water-cooling radiator.

This oil-lubrication system works this way with all aircraft engines, not just radial engines, for any aircraft might accidentally or purposely fly upside down—and this is no time for an engine failure due to improper lubrication.

There are *inverted* air-cooled and liquid-cooled engines for aircraft use, the pistons working inside the cylinders that point down rather than up. Naturally the engine does not care whether it is upside down or sideways, just as long as it receives the proper lubrication and fuel and electricity. Therefore aircraft designers often mount inverted engines to improve the streamlining on an airplane. If the airplane is so streamlined that the engine is completely closed in, air-cooled engines can still be used. In these cases, an air scoop will be visible. Air is rammed into this scoop by the propeller and then is guided around the cooling fins. If the closed-in, streamlined engine is one of the liquid-cooled models, then the air is guided by the scoop into the liquid-cooling radiator.

Air-cooled or liquid-cooled—which is best for an airplane?

This has been discussed by airplane builders and pilots for some time, for each engine has certain advantages. With air-cooling, for example, the engine can be lighter (with no water jacket to double the walls of the heads and cylinder block) and, of course, no cooling liquid is necessary. On the other hand, it is easier to streamline an airplane with an engine that is sleeker to begin with, and one that can be mounted entirely inside the body shell of the plane, as can be done more easily with a liquid-cooled engine. But the air-cooled-engine builders point out that one single bullet in the water jacket of a fighter-plane engine can disable the plane as the cooling liquid leaks out, whereas a bullet into an air-cooled engine will probably damage only one cylinder.

There are fine examples of both types, and both types are still in prominent use today. The famed *P-51 Mustang* (still in use as a stunt plane and air racer) used an in-line liquid-cooled engine. You can easily note the huge scoop under the body of the airplane that directs cooling air through the radiator. The same is true with the twin-engined *P-38 Lightning.* Both these airplanes had a dramatic combat record, particularly the *Mustang,* which many pilots still call the finest airplane ever built. There are, of course, many other excellent examples of the liquid-cooled air plane engine. The *P-47 Thunderbolt,* affectionately called "The Jug" by many fighter pilots, used an *air*-cooled engine of the radial type. So did the B-24, B-25, and B-26 light bombers, though they used two engines each.

One of the most popular, light private airplanes today is the Piper Aztec. It uses twin six-cylinder horizontally opposed air-cooled engines. These engines are completely closed in by streamlining fairings, but you can see the air-inlet scoops. The Sikorsky S-58 helicopter has a closed-in, hidden engine, yet it is of a nine-cylinder air-cooled radial type. You can see that almost any engine-type can be used with almost any airplane, depending upon what the designer thinks is best for the application he has in mind. You can tell the difference in engines, either from close up or from a distance, by looking for the cooling fins, or lack of them.

Supercharging, which is used on high-performance automobile engines, is quite important on aircraft engines and is in common use. Air is crammed into the cylinders of modern aircraft engines just as it is in automobile engines, but it is even more important, for an aircraft engine faces additional problems.

The first is altitude. The higher an airplane goes, the thinner the air becomes, so even though an engine might work fine at sea level in heavy air, it might "starve" for air as it goes up. So superchargers force more air into the engine. Without superchargers, an engine that produces 1,000 horsepower at sea level will turn out only about 370 horsepower at 25,000 feet because of the thin atmosphere.

The second problem is the great amount of air required by the large aircraft engine, or any large engine for that matter.

The air used in an internal-combustion engine must pass very rapidly through relatively small manifolds and valve ports. The 1,000-horsepower airplane engine, when running at full power, burns about 600 pounds of gasoline in an hour (about 100 gallons). To run prop-

The world's fastest helicopter, a rigid-rotor XH-51A, is powered by both a turbine engine and the obvious jet engine on the side.

The new AH-56A turbine-powered "Cheyenne" helicopter. It combines the vertical takeoff of the helicopter with the speed of a fixed-wing aircraft, and is used to "ride shotgun" for ground troops. (Lockheed-California photos)

(*Above*) Jet and rocket in action together; (*below*) turbine and rocket together. (Lockheed-California photo)

erly, it must also use *over 8,000 pounds* of air in the same period of time. This is more than 800,000 gallons of air—in one hour. An airplane-engine supercharger is used to ram this huge amount of air into the engine in this time.

The turbine engine is also a prominent aircraft engine. In fact, the engine used by Parnelli Jones at the 1967 Indianapolis 500-mile race was really an aircraft engine in disguise, which had been modified for use in a race car. This engine in Jones's racer was very likely the first step toward the engine of the future passenger car, for not only will it burn cheaper fuels, but it is also almost maintenance-free. It is lighter than the standard automobile engine and emits less air pollutants.

In an airplane turbine engine, the final drive shaft that turns the compressor blades and the turbine wheels is fastened directly to the propeller (or rotor blades of a helicopter) rather than passing into a transmission box which directs power to wheels.

Though it may be the engine of the future, turbines have an ancient history starting with Hero of Alexandria, who described the first known steam turbine in A.D. 120, as nearly as we can figure. It was a small metal globe mounted on a pipe leading from a steam kettle. Steam from the spout of the kettle passed from two L-shaped pipes fastened to opposite sides of the glove, spinning the globe around. This was the world's first "jet" engine, as far as we know.

Windmills, which came into use in the Middle East as early as A.D. 900, are a form of turbine, using air for power rather than expanding gases. The first crude gas turbines were built in the 1600s when people mounted a fan over a cooking fire to turn a roasting spit. The heat from the fire would rise, turn the blades of the fan, and, through simple gear arrangements, turn the spit.

The problem was that much of the flowing gases or fluids used to turn these early turbine wheels was escaping. So in 1832, a French engineer by the name of Benoit Fourneyron developed the first really workable *enclosed* water turbine. Fourneyron's machine developed 50 horsepower and was used to drive metal forging hammers. By 1855, A Paris waterworks had a turbine that produced 800 horsepower.

Jet-engine mechanics work on a huge fan-jet engine. (American Airlines photo)

Carl Gustav de Laval, a Swedish engineer, invented a cream separator and then, in 1883, built an impulse steam turbine to power it. One year later another improvement came when Charles A. Parsons developed a reaction steam turbine in England. Charles G. Curtis, an American, thought up the idea of using many wheels rather than just one, and so turbines increased greatly in efficiency. Curtis, who conceived his multiple-wheel idea in 1900, built the huge Curtis turbine which was installed in an electric power plant in Chicago. His turbine ran a generator that produced 5,000 kilowatts of electricity, taking up less than one tenth the space of a steam piston engine, weighing less than one eighth as much, and costing less than one third as much. And it used far less steam. The Curtis turbine was one of the greatest revolutions in the development of this form of power.

Yet it was not an internal-combustion turbine. Engineers realized the great advantage of burning gases within the turbine to make it operate, but no metal would stand the tremendous heat thus developed. It was not until World War II that such metals were formulated, and the gas turbine, as we know it, was developed.

Did you ever watch a frog jump from a little log in the water? Most of us have blown up a balloon and then let it go. In both cases, you see the principle that has developed into one of the most efficient, fastest, and safest forms of internal-combustion engines for airplanes.

The entire matter is based upon a principle first stated in 1687 by the English scientist Sir Isaac Newton. He said, "To every action there is an equal and opposite reaction."

When the frog jumps from the little log, the log moves in the opposite direction. The reaction (the log moving backwards) is equal and opposite from the action (the frog's legs pushing). The balloon soars and rushes around erratically as the air inside escapes, creating a reaction as inside pressure rushes out.

From these simple actions and principles come our modern turbojet, afterburner, and turboprop airplane engines, and the pulsejet, ramjet, and rocket. But first, exactly how does a jet engine work? Many people feel that jet propulsion is a result of hot exhaust gases "pushing" against the outside air, but this is not the case at all. In fact, jet propulsion will work just as well in a vacuum, where there is no air at all, if oxygen is provided to support the combustion of gases inside the engine.

A jet engine works on the *reaction* principal, the same as the moving log or the balloon. The engine is the log, and the exhaust is the frog. When the exhaust shoots backward into space, the reaction to this action drives the engine (and the airplane) forward.

Inside pressure is built up in a jet engine in two ways. The pressure is built by burning a fuel that expands into hot gases and by squeezing or compressing the fuel mixture. Some jets use only the first method while others use both methods together. After the pressure has been built up, it is allowed to escape to the rear, creating the action and the reaction.

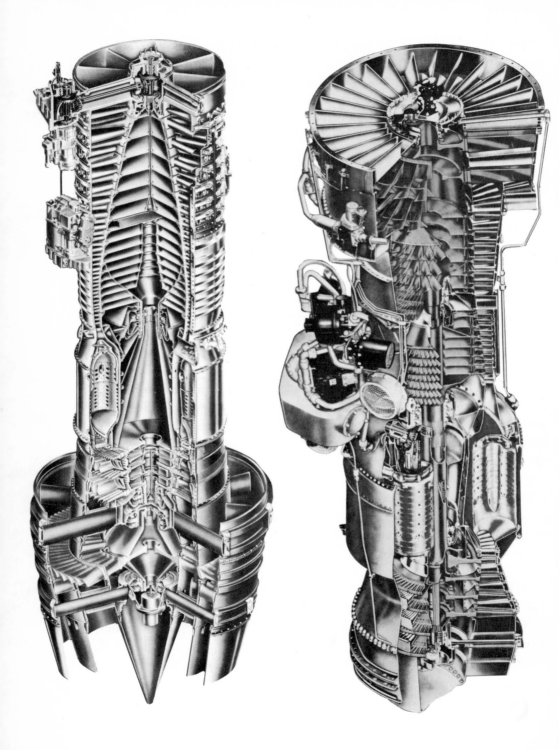

The ramjet has the simplest construction of the various types of jet engines used in aircraft, for it has no compressor wheels and no turbine wheels. The air enters the front of the engine and is guided into a narrowing tube which compresses it. Fuel is added, the mixture is ignited and burns, forcing its way out the rear and providing thrust. Once started, the burning is a continuous matter, with guards provided inside the engine so that the flame is not merely blown out with the exhaust. This engine, however, will not operate until it is traveling fast enough to ram air into the front end, a major disadvantage. Generally another engine, such as a rocket, is used to bring the ramjet up to its operating speed.

The turbojet is the most commonly used jet engine. This is the one you see on modern commercial jetliners. It is made up of a compressor, a combustion area, a turbine, and a tail pipe through which the exhaust escapes. This mighty engine can produce up to about 10,000 pounds of thrust, or forward motion, with the blade-mounted wheels inside spinning at speeds up to 15,000 revolutions per minute. No wonder they whine and thunder!

After the air is compressed by the compressor wheels, it rushes into a set of combustion chambers where the air is mixed with fuel and ignited. The expanding gases rush out the tail pipe, at the same time turning the turbine wheels which drive, through a central shaft, the compressors. These turbine wheels must be made of metals that can withstand the terrific heat inside, sometimes over 1,600 degrees! The action of the exhaust gases rushing out is what drives the engine forward.

This type of engine is started by first spinning the turbine wheels with auxiliary power, then a spark plug gets the ignition going. Once started, the fuel mixture continues to burn until the fuel supply is shut off.

Often an afterburner is mounted between the turbine wheels and the tail pipe. Many modern military planes use an afterburner to increase

(*Left*) Cutaway view of the General Electric Aft Turbofan jet engine; and (*right*) the Pratt & Whitney forward fan-jet engine. (Courtesy American Airlines)

their power and speed. This device is merely a ramjet installed in the system as described. Additional fuel is supplied to the ramjet, which is driven by the rushing gases from the turbojet. This combined power is pushed from the exhaust in a stream of superheated gases, driving the aircraft forward with much greater power than with the turbojet alone.

A propeller-driven jet airplane is called a turboprop. In this plane the propeller is attached to the shaft of the compressor wheels, which is still driven by the turbine wheels, which are still turned by the expanding hot gases. In the turboprop, however, most of the energy from the gases is expended in turning the propeller, with the remainder being jetted from the rear of the engine for additional power. Turboprop engines that can produce up to 10,000 horsepower are smaller and lighter than piston engines producing only 3,500 horsepower.

Perhaps you have heard the staccato stutter of a pulsejet engine on certain missiles or drone aircraft. This engine delivers a hair-raising sound as it thunders into life. In fact, engineers have called it such nicknames as "the stuttering stovepipe," though it is officially called an "aeroresonator" or a "intermittent-firing duct powerplant."

Officially the world's fastest airplane (spring 1968), a twin-jet-powered Lockheed YF-12A, over the rugged desert mountains of southwestern United States. Speed is "more than" 2,000 miles per hour. (Lockheed-California photo)

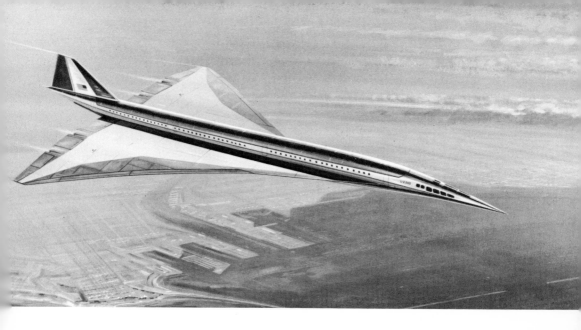

An airliner of the future, the supersonic (1,800 miles per hour) SST. It will be jet-powered. (Lockheed-California photo)

The pulsejet is simpler than the turbojet, having neither a mechanical compressor nor a turbine wheel. It is little more than a shell containing air-intake valves, a combustion chamber, and a tail pipe. Fuel is sprayed into the combustion chamber and air is forced into the air-intake valves to start the pulsejet engine. A spark ignites the fuel-air mixture, causing a rapid expansion of gases inside the combustion chamber. This pressure inside instantly closes the air-intake valves, so the only way out for the pressure is to the rear, providing thrust. As the pressure escapes, the air-inlet valves open and more air rushes in to mix with incoming fuel. The hot walls of the combustion chamber ignite the new mixture and the same sequence repeats—again and again, very rapidly (from 50 up to 250 times every second, each time with an ear-splitting blast).

You can see why it is called "the stuttering stovepipe!"

This pulsejet engine is a lightweight unit with few parts, but it does burn about three times as much fuel as the better-known and much more widely used turbojet. If you have seen a motion picture of the "blitzkreig" of London during World War II, you have probably seen and heard pulsejets in operation, for these engines powered the infamous German V-1 "buzz-bombs" of that era.

Rockets do not "breathe" in the sense that most of these jet-type engines take in air from the front, though they work in about the same way. They carry their own oxygen inside to support the burning of their fuel load, called *LOX* by rocket engineers (*l*iquid *ox*ygen). One advantage becomes quickly obvious. Where the turbojet, and other jet engines, need atmosphere in which to operate (but only to provide oxygen to support the combustion of their fuel), the rocket can streak upward until it has reached beyond the layer of air around the earth—and it can keep right on going for as long as its fuel and *LOX* supply remains otherwise, it operates in basically the same manner as any other jet, with a combustion chamber and an exhaust pipe. As you can see, when man goes to the moon and beyond (while still powered by internal-combustion engines, that is) he will use rocket power.

Perhaps by the time he is planning a trip beyond the moon, though, he will have invented newer ways to power his flying machines. Perhaps he will still use the internal-combustion idea, and perhaps not; but even if he does not, he will still have to credit man's amazing progress to the hesitant little "four-banger" developed by such pioneers as the Wright brothers, and the improvements since then. For the space vehicle that thunders away, or hums away, or whines away, or streaks silently into the dark sky, will be the direct descendent of the four-stroke-cycle internal-combustion reciprocating-piston type engine.

126

motorcycles

To be very specific, the contraption developed by old Gottlieb Daimler and ridden by his son Paul back in 1885 was a motorcycle of sorts. Yes, it had four wheels, but only two of them were functional. The other two were helper wheels, such as those you see today on a youngster's first "two-wheeler." They acted more as "landing gears" than as rolling wheels, holding the vehicle upright when stopped or at slow speeds (which was often, for the bike did not really have a *fast* speed).

But it certainly was not like the motorcycle and motorized bike engines we have today—not in design, nor power, nor efficiency, nor beauty.

Paul Daimler had to start his little one-cylinder engine by turning a huge hand crank after lighting a Bunsen burner to supply the ignition, whereas modern motorcycle engines start with a quick kick or even an electric starter. And where Paul Daimler's bike finally worked up to the high speed of ten miles per hour, modern motorcycle engines can drive motorcycles several *hundred* miles per hour.

On August 25, 1966, there appeared at the famed Salt Flats of Bonneville, Utah, a motorcycle of superb design and construction. It was a torpedo-shaped little vehicle, the streamlining shell added to cut wind resistance as much as possible, for the motorcycle was preparing to attack the world speed record for two-wheelers. At that time the record was held by rider Bill Johnson, who had streaked his motorcycle to a speed of over 230 miles per hour at the same location a couple of years before.

A 1903 Triumph single-cylinder Belgian-Minerva side-valve motorcycle. Pedal gear and clutchless belt (note "gear shift" that engages idler pulley) were common practice on early-day motorcycle engines. (Courtesy Triumph Corporation)

Designed by Alex Tremulis, the Triumph engine-powered motorcycle had *two* 650-cc engines hooked together for double the power and speed. Power was transmitted to the rear wheel by a heavy-duty chain. Projecting from each side, reminiscent of Daimler's first motorcycle, were struts to hold the bike in an upright position when parked, for with the completely enclosing body shell the rider could not merely put his legs out to hold the bike up. These struts were retractable by the driver once the motorcycle was in motion. Christened the "Gyronaut X-1" the motorcycle was a picture of precision and speed.

Driver Bob Leppan buckled himself in, started the twin engines, and headed for the measured mile of the course, picking up speed all the way. Entering the traps, he rocketed to a new world's speed record for motorcycles of over 240 miles per hour—a far cry from that attained by Daimler's first model.

Yet this was only the beginning according to the Gyronaut's designer.

Alex Tremulis predicts that his twin-engine bike is just the first in a total revolution in two-wheelers powered by internal-combustion engines. He has on the drawing board and in various stages of construction a new version which will be powered by a 9,000 pound thrust jet engine. He expects this new bike to reach the amazing speed of *750 miles per hour* on the Salt Flats. To cope with shock waves, which could buffet the bike out of control at such speeds, he is designing an "aerodynamic rake studded with needle points that will intercept the shock wave, diffuse it, and render it harmless before it strikes the rear stabilizing fin." Even then, the speed record attempt will be very dangerous—but men will always attempt to go faster.

The future of two-wheeled, internal-combustion-powered vehicles stretches on and on according to Tremulis. He is designing and building an odd two-wheeled vehicle which will be powered by internal combustion and stabilized by a gyroscope. He feels that this vehicle will be a

This old Triumph was built in 1909, and it still runs perfectly. It is a one-cylinder model owned by Frank Johnson of Lincoln, Massachusetts, and on display at the Lars Anderson Museum in Brookline, Massachusetts. (Courtesy Triumph Corporation)

forerunner of an entirely new concept in transportation in which all vehicles will have only two wheels—that everybody will be riding "motorcycles" in the future. According to this futuristic designer, the four-wheeled vehicle will fade from the scene. We should listen to his forecast, because so far he has had an accurate record for predicting vehicles of the future.

Usually when we think of motorcycles we think of the popular little one-cylinder models flooding the market today. They haul loads far above what their mild appearance indicates, and they operate dependably and without breakdown forever, so it would seem. To this point, in fact, since they are a relatively new item, their useful life cannot yet be predicted—though it will obviously run into many years.

What happened to Daimler's inefficient, unusual-appearing engine to bring it to its present state? Very little, in fact, when basic operation is considered.

Motorcycle competition has been around for years. This is the start of the 1909 Indianapolis Speedway Motorcycle Race. Fourth from left is the famed "Cannonball" Baker on an early Indian. (Indianapolis Motor Speedway photo)

Owner-builder Joe Dudek and driver Bill Johnson, previous holders of the world's land speed record for two-wheelers.

The Triumph-powered streamliner they used to attain a speed of 230.269 miles per hour. Engine is a 650-cc Triumph. (Chan Bush photos)

Both Daimler's first engine and the modern air-cooled motorcycle "one-lunger" are powered by vaporized gasoline. (Or "was" in the case of Daimler's model, as unfortunately his first model was destroyed in a museum fire many years ago.) In both cases, the vaporized gasoline burns in a compression area above a movable piston, resulting in a push against the piston by expanding gases and a thrust which turns a crankshaft. The turning crankshaft powers the bike.

So Daimler's idea was a good one, and engine builders stayed with it. But only basically.

Whereas Daimler's engine was unattractive and unwieldy, the modern one-cylinder motorcycle engine is a compact power unit which, to an engine lover, is beautiful to look at. New metals helped to decrease the size of the unit and to turn it into a much higher compression engine. With the stronger metals came a shorter piston stroke (the distance the piston travels in the bore) and thus a shorter cylinder.

The ignition system was vastly improved, for engine builders soon realized that lighting a Bunsen burner was not the answer—even if it did work for Daimler. This method was unsafe, inconvenient, and inefficient. Modern motorcycle engines use the electric ignition system familiar on automobiles, with but one exception. The motorcycle, where weight and compactness is a greater factor than in the automobile, generally utilizes the magneto system of ignition. In this system there is no storage battery in the ignition circuit (though there is a small one in the electrical system for operating the horn and lights). The ignition system is dead in a magneto circuit until the engine is cranked, or "kicked" by the starting pedal. This spins the magneto, which provides a current to the spark plug inside the cylinder. The spark plug ignites the fuel, the expanding gas mixture pushes the piston, turning the crankshaft, which is geared to the magneto.

So when the crankshaft spins, the magneto spins, and more electrical current is generated. Once started, the engine keeps running, or at least continues to provide current until something else stops it. The main switch (usually in the form of a key and lock) is in the magneto circuit, so when the switch is turned off the circuit is broken. No more current flows and the engine stops. Racing bikes (and, indeed, many other racing vehicles) often have a "dead man's" switch. This aptly named main ignition switch is attached into the ignition and throttle circuit. It must be held to be activated. If the pressure is released, as in an accident or if a rider falls off, the system shuts itself off.

132

Steeplechase racing! If the lead man's wheel collapses, and it *does* happen, a grinding crash is on! Site is Ascot Speedway in Los Angeles. (Chan Bush Photo)

Modern motorcycle engines are either two-stroke-cycle units or four-stroke-cycle units, with the trend to the two-stroke-cycle engine (with Honda as the notable exception to this trend), at least where "light" motorcycles (up to 300-cc) are concerned.

So, although they all work on the reciprocating principle, they are somewhat different in operation. The two-stroke-cycle engine ignites its fuel mixture *each time* the piston reaches the compression point in the cylinder, while the four-stroke-cycle engine ignites its mixture *every other* time.

There can be certain problems with the modern two-stroke-cycle internal-combustion engine that are not present in any other type unit. This is primarily because two-stroke-cycle engines, regardless of the number of cylinders, burn oil in the fuel mixture for lubrication.

One rider started off on a short trip on his modern little motorcycle but before he had gone five miles the bike seemed to lose power. It would run, and sounded fine while idling alongside the road, but the instant power was applied the little engine would struggle and finally die. The indication was "flooding," or too much fuel entering the combustion chamber—which is another common trait with these two-stroke-cycle engines. But checking the choke and finally disassembling the carburetor (this can be done, for one of the real advantages of these small two-stroke-cycle engines is that they can be worked on anytime, any place, they are so uncomplicated) proved nothing.

The ignition? Everything seemed normal, and a simple test indicated a lively spark at the correct time. He had fuel, and he had electricity.

Finally the rider thought to check the *muffler,* of all things, thinking that a back pressure in the exhaust system might be causing the trouble. The muffler looked fine. It had a coating of black carbon on it, of course, but that was to be expected in the oil-burning engine. So he rechecked the other items in the engine once again, but still the engine refused to operate even though everything appeared normal.

Finally, in desperation, he once again removed the muffler core and this time he scraped away the very thin coating of carbon from around the baffles inside. With little optimism, he replaced the part and restarted the engine.

It ran like a brand new wrist watch—with which many of these little engines favorably compare. When everything is right, they will run on almost forever, but if one little item goes sour, they will not run at all. The thin coating of carbon in the muffler core was restricting the flow of exhaust gases just enough to indicate a flooding condition, even though the malfunction had nothing to do with incoming fuel.

Of course to give credit where credit is due, almost every manufacturer's handbook suggests a muffler cleaning every so often to prevent this very thing from happening to a two-stroke-cycle engine. The rider had ignored the instruction—until that day alongside the road.

On the other hand, a multiple-cylinder engine of the four-stroke-cycle type can run with many things wrong. It may not run just right, but it probably will run long enough to get you home or to a garage. Once three young men were driving between cities in Louisiana, at an early morning hour. In this almost deserted bayou country, help can be a long time in coming if you break down.

But the car did break down, and solidly. Inside the engine a connecting rod snapped, though fortunately it did not swing around and damage the block of the engine. Naturally the car came to a grinding, clanking halt.

The engine happened to be an in-line six-cylinder model, and it was one of the center connecting rods that had broken. The driver considered the matter and made a decision which would obviously never work with any one- or two-cylinder engine. With the help of his friends, he drained the oil from the engine, removed the oil pan (exposing the crankshaft), then removed the entire rod and piston assembly from that cylinder. Since it was ruined anyhow, further bending and breaking (and there *was* some!) did not matter. Then he put everything back in place, leaving the one cylinder empty.

Not only did the engine start and run on five cylinders (though slowly and roughly, for it was then quite out of balance), but it ran all the way to a garage several miles on down the road.

Motorcycle-engine builders soon realized that if one cylinder would do the job, then two would do it better.

A drag bike in action! This specially built engine will drive the bike from 0 to 60 miles per hour in only *five* seconds. (Chan Bush photo)

A typical 80-cc one-cylinder light motorcycle engine of the popular sports class. Note cooling fins on the cylinder block and head of this air-cooled engine. (Photo by author)

Spark-plug conditions in a two-stroke-cycle engine: (*top, right*) Normal; insulator is light tan or brown, and light combustion deposits may be sticking to the insulator and shell bore. Electrode erosion not excessive. (*top, left*) Carbon fouling; heavy, black, carbon-like deposits on electrode and insulator, often result of over-rich running or improper fuel-oil mixture, or too "cold" a plug. (*bottom, left*) Oil fouling; too much oil in the gasoline. (*bottom, right*) Burning; electrodes show evidence of far too much heat. (Courtesy Champion Spark Plug Company)

Then four, then six, then *eight,* for there are actually eight-cylinder motorcycle engines for use on such motorcycles as "drag bikes."

Certainly one- or two-cylinder engines are in the great majority for motorcycle use, but these eight-cylinder jobs are exciting to see in action. They rumble up to the starting line of a drag strip and when the light on the "Christmas Tree" flashes green they streak away in an almost unbelievable display of pick-up. All the while they are shooting a fountain of smoke high up into the air from a burning, spinning rear tire. Of course the rider must carefully control the engine's speed and power output or the bike will merely "walk over" on top of him by first rising up on its rear wheel and then tipping over backwards, so great is the potential power and getaway.

Motorcycles have been manufactured with drive shafts connecting the engine to the wheel, but usually a chain is used. This chain is the refinement of the earlier belt drives which began to fail as engine power increased. The chain takes the power off the end of the crankshaft (through a transmission with several "speeds") and to the rear wheel sprocket. A clutch, very much like the clutch in any vehicle, smooths and regulates the power and allows the engine to disengage from the wheel while the vehicle is standing with its engine running.

Motorcycle internal-combustion engines may be standard in one- or two-cylinder models, but there the similarity ends. They come in all shapes and sizes, depending upon the job they are designed to do. They come as small as about 50 cc and up to about 1,200 cc or more.

They are all, however, air-cooled (notice the cooling fins on the cylinders) with only very rare exceptions.

This "cc" (cubic centimeter) measurement is interesting. Whereas the "compression ratio" of an internal-combustion engine is the difference in the volume of fuel mixture before and after compression, the measurement in cubic centimeters (or cubic inches in larger engines) is the amount of space inside the cylinder used by the stroke of the piston. This has nothing to do with pressure, as in compression ratio, but is rather a strict measurement of internal size. This figure is arrived at by multiplying the bore (the diameter of the cylinder) by the stroke (the distance the piston travels), and is used in virtually every internal-combustion engine as a measurement of size.

Perhaps you have heard, for example, of the "three-liter rule" for cars in certain races. This, again, is a measurement of space inside the cylinders of the engine. It does not matter how many cylinders there are, just so the total measurement inside the entire combination does not exceed three liters. They use this displacement figure, of course, to assure equalization among cars. One builder might choose to use eight small cylinders and another four larger ones, while both have the same total displacement.

A 50-cc Honda engine would be slightly smaller than an 80-cc Yamaha engine, and both would be far smaller than a workhorse 1,200-cc Harley-Davidson engine, even though all three work in basically the same manner. The larger the displacement figure of an engine, the larger the size and (generally) the higher the power.

Obviously, for example, if you were to increase the bore of any engine, you would also increase the displacement and the resulting power, all other things being equal. This is one way, in fact, of "souping up" an engine. A skilled mechanic can hone a cylinder bore to a larger size by

The world's fastest motorcycle (spring 1968), and crew. Left to right, Driver Bob Leppan, Designer Alex Tremulis, Sponsor Jim Bruflodt, and three crew members. (Courtesy *Hot Rod* Magazine)

merely grinding away a layer of the inside cylinder wall; then he can install larger pistons to fill the larger cylinder, thus increasing the displacement figure of the engine. Increasing the stroke (remember, bore x stroke = displacement) is somewhat more difficult, but it also can be done to increase the power of an engine for racing or some other high-performance purpose.

Regardless of refinements though, every internal-combustion engine powering a motorcycle works in basically the same way, whether it be a little 50-cc sports-cycle engine or a huge multi-cylinder engine of high displacement such as those used by police departments. Whether they bellow or just put-put, gasoline and air are mixed in a carburetor, fed into a combustion chamber, and there ignited by a spark plug. The expanding gases that result push against a piston which turns a crankshaft, and the bike is driven. The smaller they are, the simpler they are, and the fewer moving parts they have (one very popular two-stroke-cycle light motorcycle internal-combustion engine has a total of only nine moving parts). The larger they are, the more complicated and powerful they are.

But they still all work in the same way.

boats

Every year thousands and thousands of vacationers load up their cars and head for a favorite vacation spot for some relaxation. Every single weekend thousands more relax in the same way. Often they will have a strange trailer attached behind as they leave home, a trailer designed and built to haul one single thing—a boat.

Boating as a recreational pastime has increased rapidly because boats are now available to anyone with even a modest income and boats are now quite dependable and safe.

The marine internal-combustion engine—"inboard," "outboard," or "inboard/outboard" (I/O)—has been the biggest single factor in the increase of safety and dependability. Even many who prefer sailboats will carry an engine for use in emergencies.

If you think that other means of travel have a wide variety of engines, just take a look at boats. Here you will find a range from little one-cylinder put-put engines all the way to giant engines that power ocean-going yachts. The one you can carry in one hand, the other is far larger than any automobile engine—all the way up to room-sized diesels with tremendous power.

Yet, with the exception of the diesel, they still all work basically in the same way. Fuel is admitted, ignition occurs, a piston is moved in a cylinder, and power has been made available—in this case to move a boat by turning an underwater propeller.

But again, there are also many differences in marine engines, for you cannot merely take an engine from an automobile or a power lawn mower and install it in a boat.

141

Two boating uses of the internal-combustion engine, the outboard motor and the "Air-Buoy" diver's air supply. (Johnson Motors)

First, let's clear up the terms. An "outboard" internal-combustion engine is one that is suspended over the stern. It is usually small and portable. An "inboard" engine is one that is permanently mounted within the hull of the boat and appears more like a standard automobile engine. An "I/O" is one that has the engine part (the cylinder block, pistons, and so forth) inside the hull of the boat near the transom, and the drive section outside the boat on the stern. Therefore part of the unit is inboard and part of it is outboard.

You'll never guess who invented one of the first "motorboats" in the world—though he must this time share some of the credit. Perhaps the *very* first workable motorboat, driven by an internal-combustion engine using naphtha for fuel, was designed and built by F. W. Ofeldt in the United States in about 1885. But then along came Gottlieb Daimler, and

The large and the small of modern outboard motors. ((*top*) Courtesy Johnson Motors; and (*bottom*) Kiekhaefer Mercury)

he put together and ran the first boat in the world driven by a gasoline-powered internal-combustion engine. He did this in 1887.

What a magnificent mind this German inventor must have had! First a wheeled vehicle and then a boat.

Motorboating, however, did not become practical until the early 1900s when gasoline-powered engines became somewhat more efficient. Even then, the boats were long and skinny and heavy, so they were very difficult to operate. As a sport, boating languished, for motorboats were expensive and engines still relatively unreliable.

Gradually the engines improved, as did boat hull design and construction, and in 1939 Sir Malcolm Campbell drove a hydroplane to a speed record of 141.74 miles per hour. This record set by the daring Englishman was not broken for many years, until 1952 when Stanley Sayres of Seattle, Washington, finally set a new record for propeller-driven inboard motorboats. He drove his own sleek hydroplane with its 3,000-horsepower internal-combustion engine to a speed of 178.497 miles per hour.

During this period, from about 1940 on, *outboard* motors began to gain wide public acceptance, for they were proving to be convenient and very efficient. They were also fast for their size, for the average outboard engine during the 1940s was of only 3 or 4 horsepower (although racing engines of up to about 50 horsepower had been developed in the out-

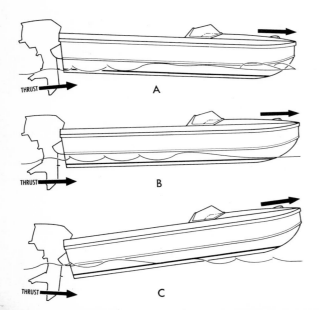

The outboard-style marine engine is mounted on the stern, the angle of mounting determining the thrust. (Courtesy McCulloch Corporation)

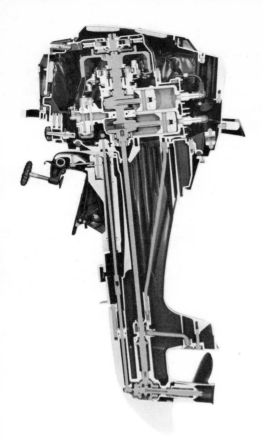

A cutaway view of a typical outboard motor. Note the twin cylinders and pistons, and the vertical shaft that transmits power to the lower unit. (Courtesy Kiekhaefer Mercury)

board class). In the late 1940s new aluminum alloys were developed, and outboard motors took a jump in both power and beauty and by the mid-50s manufacturers were building outboard engines of up to 70 horsepower for regular sporting use.

Now we see huge models of up to 100 horsepower, often mounted in "tandem" (side by side) to give almost unlimited power to any boat. The boat itself determines the size and amount of power of the engine now, for engines are available in whatever size and power is desired. Now readily available is a choice ranging from tiny little "kickers" which weigh only a few pounds all the way up to several-hundred-pound monsters which need a crane for installation.

The outboard motor is by far the most popular marine internal-

Even outboard marine internal-combustion engines have wartime uses. Here a number of them are used on an Army pontoon bridge (Courtesy Kiekhaefer Mercury)

combustion engine in the world. More people use the outboard type than any other—though this may not always hold true, for new jet-turbine and diesel engines are being produced for the hobbyists and are gaining wide public acceptance. Also, the gasoline-powered inboard internal-combustion engine has always been popular for somewhat larger boats, which are becoming more common.

Still, it is the outboard that is, today, most popular. And once again, it operates basically like any other internal-combustion engine even though in appearance it is quite different. Fuel is ignited in a combustion chamber, driving a piston and producing power. Outboards, though, are light (relatively) and portable (again, relatively), and they are almost always of the two-stroke-cycle type, which means lubricating oil must be admitted with the fuel into the cylinders.

Outboard engines come in a variety of cylinder-block styles, usually either in-line or V-type. The four-cylinder V-type is a popular model for general all-around water-sports use, with two cylinders on each side forming the V. These engines, however, are quite heavy and do not

146

really fall into the readily portable class though they can be carried by a couple of strong men.

The engine is clamped to the stern of the boat with built-on clamps, with the cylinder block and all electrical parts above the water line. This upper unit drives a vertical shaft that runs down into the lower unit of the engine containing the propeller, which is of course under water.

Inside the upper unit of the outboard internal-combustion engine are exactly the same parts as in the standard two-stroke-cycle engine, though of a particular size and conformation according to what the particular manufacturer decided was best for his own product. If you were to disassemble an outboard engine, you would find pistons, connecting rods, a crankshaft—everything you would expect to find in any internal-combustion engine. But the similarity ends there; the crankshaft turns the long shaft going to the lower unit where a gear set changes the direction of the motion and turns the propeller.

The outboard engine, like most other marine engines, is different in another respect. Unless it is air-cooled, as few of them are, it has a water jacket just as every other water-cooled engine has—but with the unlimited supply of water available around every marine engine, no radiator is used. The cooling system is an *open* circuit. The water is merely pumped from the water in which the boat is operating. It circulates through the engine's water jacket, cooling it, and then it is pumped overboard again. If you watch an outboard in action, you will see the stream of water jetting out just beneath the cylinder-block unit. This water will be warm to the touch, having circulated around the hot block.

Since the outboard engine of today has been built of aluminum alloys, it will tolerate use in salt water without heavy corrosion, although every marine engine should always be flushed with fresh water after use in the ocean to remove salt from the system. The ease with which an outboard can be hauled from lake to river to ocean, and back again, wherever the boatman decides to use it, is one of the major reasons for its great popularity.

The *inboard* marine internal-combustion engine is much more similar to the standard automobile engine in appearance, but it too has certain important differences. External appearance, in fact, is almost exact if we do not consider the "wet manifolds" of most inboard engines, but these manifolds are not actually a part of the basic engine.

Inside, however, the engine is built stronger, because a marine engine is often called upon to run at high-power settings for extended periods of cruising, while an automobile engine might run at nearly full power only a very small percentage of the time. Inside, the parts are stronger and heavier, and they are often braced in extra places. The pistons are thicker, and the rods and crankshaft heavier and more solidly mounted. The inboard marine internal-combustion engine is most often a V-8 type, with four cylinders on each side just as in the standard V-8 automobile engine. Mounted across the valley (over the top of the V) is the carburetor on the intake manifold, which directs the fuel mixture to the intake valves of each cylinder.

The inboard marine internal-combustion engine, appearing much like a standard automobile engine, is lowered into the hull of the boat, generally just aft of amidships, and is then hooked to a transmission which in some cases, depending upon the size of the boat, is a "reduction-type" unit. This is nothing more than a set of gears that allows the propeller shaft to revolve slower than the final output speed of the engine. The propeller shaft, projecting from the other side of the transmission, passes through the bottom of the boat by going through a "stuffing box" (which seals the opening) and a "shaft log" (which aligns the shaft properly).

On the underwater end of the shaft, which passes through one or more stabilizing "struts," the propeller is mounted.

Topside, another item that makes the engine a true marine engine is added. "Wet manifolds" are attached in the place of the regular exhaust manifolds. Both types of manifold are on an engine to carry away exhaust gases, but the wet manifold has a further job. Instead of simple pipes, or a simple casting, to carry away the exhaust, these block-like structures of cast iron accept both the exhaust gases and the *water* that has circulated to cool the engine. This water, injected into the manifolds after its job has been done, is carried out of the boat along with the exhaust gases. If you will look at the exhaust pipes projecting from the stern of most cabin cruisers while the engine is running, you will see water being exhausted. This water has been taken into the engine through an intake duct on the bottom of the boat, drawn in by a water pump alongside the engine.

A few marine engines do have closed water-systems, especially where use in salt water is planned, for ocean water is quite corrosive and can, over a period of time, ruin an engine. Most installations in sport or pleasure boats are, however, of the open type described. A few boatmen with open-water-system engines have devised a method of flushing their inboard engines with fresh water after each salt-water run, considerably lengthening the lives of the inside parts. Naturally, whether it be salt or fresh water, a certain amount of water does remain in the water jackets after the engine has been shut down. Better it be fresh than salt, so these boatmen add a shut-off valve at the salt-water-intake pipe and an inlet valve through which they can introduce fresh water for a period of running before final shut-down.

The propeller on a large boat equipped with a reduction transmission does not turn as fast as the engine is turning, so that both the engine and the propeller can turn at their most efficient speeds. If the propeller were turning at the speed of the engine on a high-rpm ocean run, it could just churn the water and lose a great deal of efficiency; yet the engine will suffer if required to run at a much slower speed for an extended time, and thereby lose efficiency—so a reduction transmission is installed. In

A typical I/O installation from the stern. Note only the drive unit is outboard, with the remainder of the engine inside the hull. (Courtesy Tollycraft Corporation)

Cutaway drawing of a typical I/O engine and drive unit. (Courtesy Kiekhaefer Mercury)

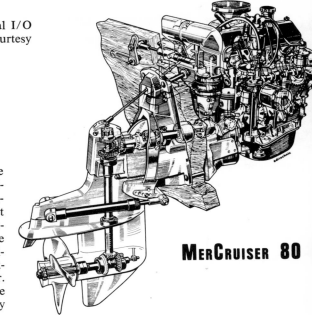

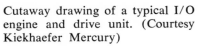

A typical inboard marine four-stroke-cycle internal-combustion engine. This engine is rated at 325 hp at 4,200 rpm, and has a compression ratio of 8.8:1. Note the huge block-like wet manifolds which accept both exhaust and cooling water. Power take-off is from the right side in photo. (Courtesy Kiekhaefer Mercury)

both a reduction transmission and a direct-drive transmission, a reverse gear is installed so that the skipper can back his boat when necessary.

The inboard marine engine uses the four-stroke-cycle principle of Gottlieb Daimler. It has an oil reservoir in the bottom of the engine, from which oil is pumped to the working parts of the engine just as the oil is pumped in the standard automobile engine.

It is possible to convert a standard passenger-car internal-combustion engine to marine use. The engine might not be as strong as desired, but otherwise it works well. Marine-style manifolds are added, along with other marine parts, when the engine is converted to boating use—or the engine is merely installed with its standard closed water-system intact and a "heat exchanger" is added to cool the fresh water with water from the lake, river, or ocean. But in either case, certain other changes are necessary, including replacing steel core plugs with brass plugs in the water jacket, leveling the carburetor (for the marine engine sits at a downward angle), adding a "flame arrestor" to the carburetor (to prevent explosions in the bilge in the event of a "backfire" in the carburetor), changing the flywheel housing, and relocating certain low-mounted standard items, such as the starter motor and generator, out of the bilge water.

The inboard/outboard is an internal-combustion installation that has the advantages of both inboard and outboard engines. Let us consider what often happens to an inboard cruiser in shallow water, or in water filled with harbor flotsam and jetsam. The boat strikes the bottom or a submerged log, the propeller and shaft are bent or broken—and the boat is dead in the water, with the damaged parts out of the reach of the skipper. He cannot repair them, for they are all under the boat. With an outboard motor, if the motor has not simply just "bounced over" the object, the propeller and bottom unit can be raised for repair, such as the replacement of the convenient "shear pin" used on many outboard motors.

The boat is not stranded if the skipper has any mechanical knowledge at all—and he *should* have, before he ever leaves port!

Yet the inboard engine is more powerful, more stable, stronger, and uses much less fuel for operation. It is more convenient, since oil need not be mixed with the gasoline, and it is certainly more "sophisticated." But being dead in the water quickly overcomes all these fine features.

Suppose, thought one boat builder, it was possible to combine the good features of both engines. By placing an inboard engine in the boat, with all its good features, and then placing the drive unit outside, nearly every disadvantage of both units could be overcome. The only disadvantage to this was that the engine would not be portable, as with the outboard engine; but really the huge outboard engines in this power class are not truly portable anyhow. So he tried it.

The inboard/outboard (I/O) was built and has been widely accepted. With this unit, the engine is inside the hull and offers the same advantages as the standard inboard (except that the I/O installations are somewhat smaller as a general rule). The driving unit and propeller are outside the hull on the transom, and within reach if repairs are required. Not only that, but most I/O engines have a drive unit mounted on a pivot so that, if the outside unit should strike something, it will merely bounce up and over—just as many true outboards do.

Also, the skipper can drive his boat into shallower water than he could with an inboard, for the "draft" (distance from the water line to the lowest point of the boat underwater) is less with an I/O than with an inboard.

diesel engines

In 1913 a German mechanical engineer embarked upon an ocean voyage on a German ship bound for London, England. Somewhere along the way he mysteriously vanished. Nobody ever saw him again, nor figured the reason for his disappearance. It was assumed that he just fell overboard on a dark night and drowned, for he was a famous man with no known enemies and a legion of friends. He had become famous as the inventor of an internal-combustion engine that was simple in design, economical in fuel consumption, and that today quite often replaces the gasoline-powered engine in many applications—even passenger cars.

This engine is considered to be one of the most efficient of all the fuel burners, since it converts to motive power more of the useful energy stored in fuel than the steam engine, the steam turbine, or the gasoline engine. You can hardly go out on the streets today without seeing a vehicle utilizing one of these engines, for they power most of the buses, trucks, and other heavy-duty equipment in the country. They are also used in ships and in railroad engines, wherever a heavy job must be done in the cheapest, most efficient manner, and where engine weight is not a prime factor (though one light-weight model was even used in a racing car to set a new speed record at Indy in the 1950s).

You will know the type of engine (if you have not already guessed it) when you hear the name of the engineer who disappeared from the ship that night in 1913. The engine has proudly carried his name ever since.

This is a rear view of a Cummins Diesel mounted in a Dodge tilt van truck. This engine is a six-cylinder, valve-in-head with a horsepower rating of 220 at 2,100 rpm. The compression ratio is a high 15.5 to 1.

The man was Rudolf Diesel.

Born in Paris of German parents, he received his education in Munich. His thoughts finally turned to designing an internal-combustion engine that would be cheaper and more efficient than those being built by Daimler, for instance. He based his ideas on the "heat-engine" principle, and in 1892 he patented his first plans. By 1897 he had a working model, and by 1913, at the time of his disappearance, he had a factory producing models regularly.

But it was not all that easy, either. Diesel learned from the famed von Linde, the first man to liquefy air, that the steam engine then in popular use was inefficient and wasted a great deal of fuel. Von Linde was a teacher in the college in Munich which Diesel attended in 1893. As a result of his conversations with von Linde and his own ideas on internal-engine efficiency, Diesel first invented an engine that used as fuel *powdered coal* which was blown into the cylinder by compressed air. He was seriously injured the first time he attempted to start this engine when it blew up in his face.

154

After an extensive period of recovery from the accident, Diesel continued his experiments, which finally led to the liquid-fuel engine that now bears his name.

Today, diesel engines are in use wherever low-cost power is desired and weight is not objectionable, for the diesel engine is heavier and bulkier than a gasoline-powered internal-combustion engine with the same power output. Yet diesels work in basically the same manner as every other internal-combustion engine—with a few important differences which makes the diesel what it is. Let's examine a diesel engine closely.

It has a cylinder block, cylinder head, crankcase, oil sump, pistons, rods, valves—everything found in a standard internal-combustion engine, but *no spark plug*. In fact, it has no electrical means of igniting its fuel at all. It does not need an electrical ignition. The diesel engine has a compression-ignition system rather than a spark-ignition system typical of the standard automobile engine.

The diesel is operated on the principle that when air in an enclosed space is suddenly compressed, the temperature of the air rises dramatically. So the fuel-air mixture is heated by compression to a sufficiently

For ease of maintenance, this Dodge LN 1000 semi-truck tractor tilts forward 55°, exposing the entire diesel unit. Note the huge four quart oil-bath air cleaner for long, dusty highway use, and the huge saddle-type fuel tanks for extended operation.

high temperature to cause it to burn, and the standard internal-combustion cycle is on. Here is exactly what happens inside the normal four-stroke-cycle diesel engine, considering one piston and one cylinder.

At first (stroke 1) the piston moves down while the air-intake valve is open, drawing air into the cylinder. On stroke 2 the piston moves upward, compressing the air and causing its temperature to rise to about 900 degrees. At the last instant, fuel is injected in a fine spray into the hot air at the top of the cylinder; this fuel burns rapidly, driving the

For great power and strength, this Cummins diesel (shown in side view in Dodge tilt van tractor-trailer unit) uses a cast iron block and head, steel forged crankshaft and camshaft, copper-lead main and conn rod bearings, and a special forged steel alloy conn rod with an I-beam section. This type diesel engine has piled up as much as 450,000 miles with only in-frame maintenance services, and many trucking firms do not even schedule them for major overhaul until 600,000 miles, in spite of the heavy work they do.

This Cummins diesel engine mounted in a Dodge LN 1000 semi-truck tractor, an in-line six-cylinder model, can haul a gross cargo weight of over seventy-six thousand pounds.

piston back down in stroke 3. At the bottom of the cylinder the piston starts back up again, moved by the force of the turning crankshaft, on stroke 4, and at the same instant the exhaust valve opens. The moving piston drives out the burned gases. Then it starts back down on stroke 1 again.

Naturally a number of pistons are working at the same time in the diesel engine, each on a different part of a different stroke, so great power is developed. Just as in the gasoline engine, the fuel in a diesel engine (which can be of a much lower grade and thus cheaper) is converted by burning to thermal, or heat, energy. The temperature inside the combustion chamber during burning goes as high as 4,500 degrees, and pressures go up to about 1,500 pounds per square inch. This is five times the pressure inside the cylinder of a gasoline-powered internal-combustion engine, so heavier, stronger, thicker parts are used in a diesel. This, of course, accounts for the weight and bulkiness of the engine.

Naturally each piston has a connecting rod to the crankshaft where the power is taken off.

157

Diesels are also built with two-stroke cycles which work very much like the two-stroke-cycle gasoline-powered engine. The exhaust and the intake of fresh air occur through ports or openings in the cylinder walls, and take place near the end of the down, or power, stroke. A two-stroke-cycle diesel does not need valves since it does not have separate exhaust and intake strokes. This one, not as popular as the better known four-stroke-cycle diesel, is used where high power is needed in a smaller engine, and where cost of operation is still important.

Aside from the fact that the diesel engine does not use spark plugs, there is another major difference.

A diesel has no carburetor. The introduction of fuel to the combustion chambers is done with an item often called the "heart" of the diesel engine. This is the fuel-injection valve which squirts a fine mist of diesel fuel into the highly compressed air inside the combustion chamber at just the right instant. This mist is produced by force-pumping a small amount of fuel through a tiny orifice in the injection valve at a very high pressure. Each cylinder has one of these valves, located very much as the spark plugs are in a standard gasoline-powered engine. The valves simply screw into openings in the cylinders at the ends of the combustion chambers.

But rather than a spark, each valve provides a shot of fuel, which is instantly ignited by the heat inside the cylinder-head area. If this precision valve should fail to provide the fuel at the exact instant it is needed, or fail to provide the correct amount, or become clogged, the engine would not run—so the fuel-injection valves are indeed very important to the diesel engine.

A diesel is cooled in the same way as the standard engine is, by cooling water being circulated through a water jacket surrounding the hot block and head.

Getting a diesel engine started is a bit more complicated than simply pushing a button. With the tremendous compression developed inside, it would take a huge electric motor to turn a diesel crankshaft and get the engine going. Different manufacturers have developed different methods of starting. In automobile engines, which are relatively small diesels, it is simply a matter of a heavier starting motor using a higher voltage to provide the power to overcome the high compression. One manufacturer of heavy-equipment diesels has built a compression-release control into his engine. The release valve partially opens each cylinder so that the operating compressions are not built up as the engine is first turned over. Then, when the engine is turning over fast enough (but not yet running), the valve is closed and the engine starts. If it does not, you just repeat the action until it does.

Perhaps the most common way to start a diesel is by utilizing the gasoline-powered internal-combustion engine. On a great number of the really heavy-duty diesel engines, which power giant earth-movers and tracked vehicles (such as those used in the Army to pick up and haul away a disabled *50-ton tank*), an auxiliary engine is installed. This conventional gasoline-powered engine is started first in the normal way and then, at the flip of a lever, is geared directly to the huge diesel engine. The little one turns the big one over and when it starts, the smaller one is turned off.

Often diesel engines are used to turn giant electrical generators, which in turn provide electricity to electric motors, and these motors do the actual work—such as in locomotives. The diesel is used because extra weight is not a disadvantage when the great power needed to turn a huge generator can be had so economically. There are also marine applications, particularly in working boats such as tugs or commercial fishing boats or larger ships, for again weight is not a primary factor considering the tremendous power and reliability of the engine, and the economy of operation.

rotary engines

Is this the end of the development of internal-combustion engines? Not at all. In fact, it is only the beginning, for as Daimler and Lenoir and de Rochas worked on the principle of converting heat energy to mechanical energy inside an engine, modern inventors and scientists are still working—and the end is far from sight. Perhaps it will never come, for men will always attempt to improve upon present devices.

The standard internal-combustion engine as we know it has performed well, but it is not, perhaps, the "best" or the "final" edition. Even though the conventional type of engine smoothly powers modern automobiles and trucks, the diesel type provides great power for heavy jobs, the racing type gives speeds of hundreds of miles per hour, and the aircraft type does what it is called upon to do, there are still others which certain engineers are now calling "the *real* engine of the future."

There are, in fact, many others, though most of them operate on what has come to be known as the "rotary" principle. And they are not really "modern," though they are just now gaining real prominence. The first true rotary engine, for example, was one built by Italian Agostino Ramelli in 1588. It was a water-pump rather than an internal-combustion type, but it was a true, eccentric, rotary machine—and is today the basis for modern exhaust-emission control devices.

The Scottish steam-power pioneer, James Watt, proposed a rotary steam engine as early as 1759—again, not an *internal*-combustion engine, but closer to it than Ramelli's water-pump design.

A rotary engine now under development by Isuzu in Japan, with a trochoidal rotor running in a three-lobe track, is based upon inventor John F. Cooley's patents of 1903. As early as 1911 the Swiss machine-tool company Oerlikon was working on a rotary engine.

Yet, today, few people really understand what a rotary engine is, or upon what principle it functions. Could this strange little engine with rotating pistons, or curved pistons, or vane-type pistons, or orbiting pistons, or scissor-action pistons (depending upon the particular model) actually be the auto engine of the future?

One of them, the Wankel, is already in production and is being installed in one model of the German-made NSU (the RO 80). It is also being tested for use in the Japanese Mazda automobile and the French Citroen. Automobile engineers and test drivers are enthusiastic about these combinations, suggesting that this type of engine will eventually replace the reciprocating-piston engine. They say that the rotary runs quieter with a smoother idle, gives much better fuel-consumption figures, and emits less exhaust pollutants. They say the engine is far smaller and lighter, yet provides the same power as a larger piston-type engine.

Strong claims? They certainly are. Let's examine how this type of engine runs.

Where the standard reciprocating-piston internal-combustion engine runs with the pistons going in an "up-and-down" motion, the rotary's pistons (or vanes, and so forth) run in a *circular* motion, or back-and-forth in a circular track. Remember the free-piston engine? Just curve the track (and take the power off mechanically rather than from compressed air) and you have a basic idea of the functioning of at least some of these rotary engines.

And there are a number of them, all competing against each other, with each inventor claiming that his model is the best and most efficient of the lot. Naturally, as time passes, some of them will drop by the wayside as faults are uncovered during extended operation, but the truth is that each of the following have so far operated smoothly and with relative efficiency. These are not drawing-board conceptions, but actual

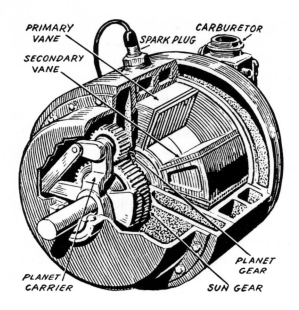

PRIMARY VANE
SECONDARY VANE
SPARK PLUG
CARBURETOR
PLANET GEAR
SUN GEAR
PLANET CARRIER

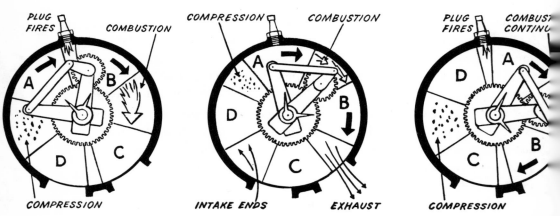

PLUG FIRES
COMBUSTION
COMPRESSION

COMPRESSION
COMBUSTION
INTAKE ENDS
EXHAUST

PLUG FIRES
COMBUST CONTINU
COMPRESSION

working engines. All they lack is extended testing under actual working conditions.

Prominent among the rotary engines now being developed is the Kauertz engine. This engine has vane-type "pistons" in a circular working chamber. Two pairs of vanes, sealed inside the circular chamber,

162

spin on the same axis but continuously change position relative to each other. This changing of position inside the chamber as the whole unit is spinning, with one set of vanes at first slowing down and then speeding up, changes the volume of fuel-air mixture between the sets of vanes, providing for compression before ignition. Then, as the mixture is ignited by a spark plug, the space between the particular two vanes on the power stroke opens as one vane is driven away from the other. Meanwhile, the remaining two vanes are approaching the ignition point in the circular chamber, closing together to give compression to a new fuel mixture. Correct position and phasing of the vanes is assured by a gear-and-crank system outside the chamber, working off the central shaft (which is also the power take-off point).

The pumping action of the vanes provides the intake and exhaust. The secondary set of vanes is alternately catching up to and then falling behind the primary set of vanes inside the engine, and the central shaft turns. The entire action is sealed by free-riding blades held against the "cylinder-block" housing by centrifugal force.

There are no valves as we know them (thus no camshafts, no cam followers, no push-rods, and no other valve-train mechanisms). The vanes open and close ports with reliable timing. The Kauertz has far fewer moving parts than the standard reciprocating engine, one of the great advantages of all rotary engines.

This engine was invented by Eugene Kauertz, who lives in retirement in Huefingen in southern Germany. Even now there are plans for full production in South Africa and by Hi Powr' Roto in Canada. And there are other firms planning to produce the Kauertz engine.

"A practical Tschudi, for example, needs *two* toroids."

Greek? No, but perhaps a language for future internal-combustion mechanics, for the Tschudi is another of the rotary engines currently under practical development and challenging the leadership of the Wankel. And it does, indeed, need two toroids for smooth, practical operation.

The toroid is the curved, enclosed track in which the four curved pistons of the Tschudi operate. Diametrically opposed, the pistons are

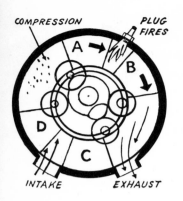
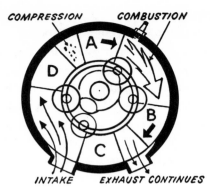
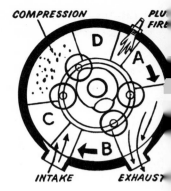

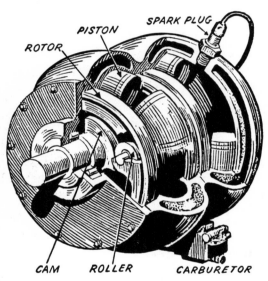

The Tschudi rotary engine.

carried on a rotor, two to each rotor. Rollers attached to the rotors bear against cams fixed to the power-output shaft. Compression is built up between the pistons, much like the operation of the Kauertz, with the cam and roller action controlling piston motion. One set of pistons stops, the other set closes in, and compression results. With ignition, the first set of pistons accelerates rapidly in the toroid, transmitting the motion to the drive shaft. The sequence continually repeats. Since each toroid pro-

164

duces two (not four) power impulses per output-shaft revolution, it takes two toroids for smoothest operation.

This engine was actually designed in 1927, the last year in the great life of the Ford Model T "Tin Lizzie," by Swiss engineer Traugott Tschudi. Of course, it has been improved greatly since then.

Rotary engines come in different styles just as reciprocating-piston engines are built in V-shapes, in-lines, radials, and horizontals. Rotaries can be broken down into four main groups also: scissor-action types with pistons or vanes, eccentric-rotor styles, multi-rotor types, and revolving-block engines. The Kauertz and the Tschudi are scissor-action rotary engines, the first with vanes and the second with pistons.

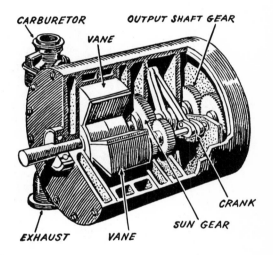

The Virmel rotary engine.

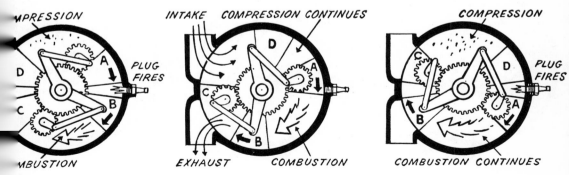

The third prominent rotary in this classification is the Virmel. Designed by Melvin Rolfsmeyer ("Vir" for his wife Virginia, "mel" for himself), the Virmel is now under development by the Lynx Corporation in Lincoln, Nebraska, for use in automobiles and boats.

This engine has two sets of vane-type pistons and a gear-and-crank system which controls vane action. In the Virmel, which works much like the Kauertz engine, the vanes come to a full stop, if only momentarily, twice during each cycle. You will recall, if you can keep up with these highly technical operations, that in the Kauertz the primary vanes

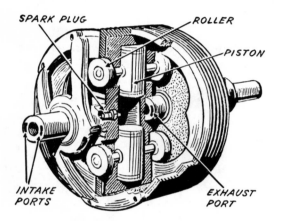

The Mercer rotary engine (a rotating-block rotary engine).

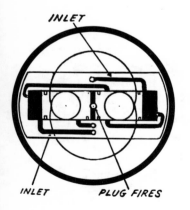

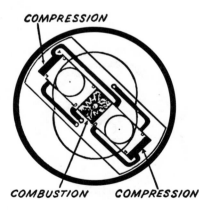

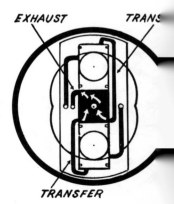

The Selwood rotary engine.

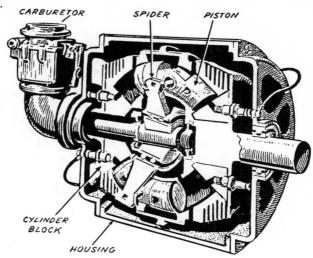

CARBURETOR SPIDER PISTON

CYLINDER
BLOCK

HOUSING

run at a steady speed and the secondary vanes vary, but neither comes to a full halt. In the Virmel (which does stop, but only as instantly as the piston stops at the top of the cylinder in the standard internal-combustion engine), power is taken off via satellite gears (and crank-shafts revolving at satellite speed) to another gear train. The satellite gears simultaneously orbit and rotate, as you can see in the diagram.

The Wankel engine is of the eccentric-rotor type and so is the Jernaes, a leading competitor. Developed by Norwegian inventor Finn Jernaes, the latter engine works almost exactly like the Wankel, but with a novel gear arrangement (see diagram). Jernaes claims that his gear mechanism increases the torque (turning power) of the engine at lower revolutions per minute. The four-stroke-cycle, single-rotor Jernaes engine produces the same number of power impulses per output-shaft revolution as a six-cylinder piston engine does.

Other leading eccentric rotor-type rotary engines are the Curtiss-Wright, the Toyo Kogyo, the Rotom, and the Isuzu. Perhaps one day these names will be as common and recognizable as Ford, Chevrolet, and Plymouth. Certainly the Wankel eccentric-rotor engine is already approaching the fringes of this popularity (especially in Europe) and

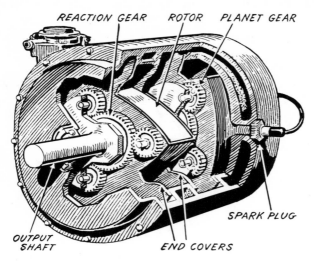

REACTION GEAR　　ROTOR　　PLANET GEAR

The Jernaes rotary engine.

SPARK PLUG

OUTPUT
SHAFT　　　　　　END COVERS

Curtiss-Wright is a well-known name in aircraft. All of these engines are in advanced stages of development, with operating models already built and with several in constant operation on test blocks (or, in the case of the Wankel in particular, in automobiles.)

In the multi-rotor type of rotary engine falls the Walter, the Scheffel, and the Walley. The principle of this type is even more technical, but basically a builder uses multiple rotors to obtain positive displacement of the gases by the interaction of the rotors in permanent contact with each other inside a close-clearance housing. The Walter uses one small and one large oval-shaped rotor inside a keyhole-shaped housing. This engine was designed in 1957 by Helmuth Walter, who was also the inventor of the Walter rocket motor. C. E. Walley chose the same principle for his rotary engine, but used four oval-shaped rotors. Walter Scheffel of Weissenburg, Germany, uses *nine* rotors in his engine, a very complicated machine indeed, but one that shows great promise.

In 1898 an inventor by the name of F. O. Farwell designed an engine with a rotating *block;* that is, the pistons move inside and turn the whole piston housing as well. The diagrams will show how the Mercer engine, one of the modern revolving-block units based upon Farwell's design,

168

functions. The other leaders in this type of rotary engine are Selwood and Porsche.

Porsche? Yes, the famed sports-car builders of Stuttgart, Germany, patented a crankless engine in 1963. It had a four-cylinder, cruciform block that revolves in a cage, getting its power from inward strokes of its roller pistons, each of which is connected by belt-like links to other rollers that are in permanent contact with a two-lobe cam on the central power-output shaft.

The builders of reciprocating-type internal-combustion engines, the type with which we are most familiar, realize that a slight change in the intake or exhaust port openings, an almost microscopic alteration, can make a substantial difference in the total performance of the engine. The same is true with the location of the spark plug in the combustion chamber, or with the ignition timing, or with the shape of the camshaft eccentric lobes. The shape of the head of a piston, or the shape of the combustion chamber, can determine how well a particular engine will run. You may have heard of the famed "hemi-head" engine of Chrysler, and the great power which resulted from this shape.

The shape of the combustion chamber seems to be the major problem with today's rotary engines. Where it is no longer difficult to develop such an engine, it is still very difficult to make it perform correctly for an extended period of time. Rotary-engine builders have not yet learned all the details about their creations. One engine may eventually show up

Four types of rotary actions.

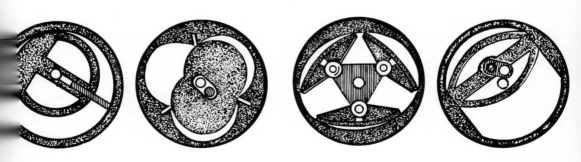

with linkages that will not carry the load over long operating periods, and another may put too much stress on its cams and rollers, and thus fail.

Where on a hot-test stand they may run well, they may fail when put under a load for testing in actual operating circumstances—except, apparently, in the case of the Wankel, which is now performing in automobiles on the roads.

But the very first, or second, or *fiftieth* reciprocating-type internal-combustion engine did not work flawlessly either. Problems continually developed, and they were solved, as men learned more and more about this particular form of engine. Now they are standard, and yet even today engine builders continue to modify and improve internal-combustion engines, and they will continue to do so for as long as we need this type.

The rotary-type internal-combustion engine could well be the engine of the future, if development continues at the present pace, and proven figures on paper turn into actual performance figures in a working engine—under working conditions.

Meanwhile, when speaking of the rotary as an engine for every single passenger car in the world, Kenichi Yamamoto, who is the guiding hand behind Japan's leading rotary (the Toyo Kogyo) insists that "the future isn't very far away."

engines of the future

Reciprocating-piston internal-combustion engine . . . turbine engine
. . . rotary engine . . . jet engine. . . ?

Perhaps we should all turn back to steam, and several engine builders
are suggesting just that. Or, what about electricity?

There is, and probably will be for many, many years, one major drawback to all internal-combustion engines, regardless of type. They all burn
a fuel mixture, and this burning creates poisonous gases and hydrocarbons that are exhausted from the engine. In an enclosed, unventilated
space, these gases can kill. But the major result when this combusted gas
mixture leaves the engine and enters the atmosphere can be "smog."

To a greater or lesser degree, every single internal-combustion engine
creates smog. This is an eye-stinging, lung-burning combination of
"smoke and fog," which at the very least is unpleasant and at the worst,
according to doctors, can cause serious illness. Most obvious in major
cities, particularly where warm, unmoving air is present, smog appears
as a yellowish haze that seems to cling to everything. From an airplane
above, a "smog bowl" obscures the ground completely. From a distance
on the ground, a layer of smog can be quite evident ahead, and one can
tell the moment he enters it, for at that moment an unpleasant odor fills
the air and the eyes begin to burn and water.

Of course, other forms of combustion contribute to any smog condition and, in fact, certain engineers insist that the internal-combustion
engine is *not* the primary cause. Many large cities forbid burning in

Two views of modern internal-combustion V-8-style engines. (Courtesy Chrysler Corporation)

incinerators and control smoke from factories. If a "smog alert" is called when a certain amount of hydrocarbons has been found in the air, many cities require factories to switch from oil to natural gas or to shut down all burning for the duration of the alert. According to a recent survey, New York City leads the field with smog, followed closely by Pittsburgh, Los Angeles, and other cities. European cities now have the same conditions as motor-vehicle traffic and industry increases.

Obviously something must be done before the population strangles itself on man-made fumes. But the answer may not be banning of all internal-combustion engines.

Imagine, for example, what would happen if every person in the world were suddenly refused the right to start any internal-combustion engine. Most immediately, all private traffic and nearly all transportation would come to a halt. Generators driven by gasoline- and diesel-powered engines would stop, and so current would no longer flow in many wires. Airplanes would be grounded, ships would be docked, mines would be flooded, as pumps stopped, diesel-powered trains would stop, emergency power could not be used in hospitals or in other critical situations—most of these are powered by internal-combustion engines.

The truth is, without internal-combustion engines, we cannot live the way we do. Now that we have them, we must keep them, for they do an infinite number of things for us aside from merely powering the family car.

Yet we know that if the harmful emissions from internal-combustion engines are not controlled, the earth may one day be surrounded by unbreathable gases. This is in the future, of course, but the trend is already evident in larger cities. To make matters worse, the trend is also for cities to become larger and larger. One group of scientists recently suggested that in a very few years over 80 per cent of the entire population of the United States will live in only *three* major cities. These sprawling cities will surround and go far beyond what we now know as the Los Angeles—San Diego area, the Chicago area, and the New York—Boston area. If we have a smog problem now in these areas, what is it going to be like if 80 per cent of all the people live in them?

Scientists and engineers are fighting the worsening smog problem in a variety of ways. Many of them are approaching it by suggesting steam-driven engines as replacements for internal-combustion engines (even though an external heat source will still have to be provided, perhaps in the form of electricity or some other non-smog-producing fuel). Remember the name "Stanley Steamer"? This was an automobile driven by steam, and it worked very well. Some engineers are trying to develop a modern version of the famous old Stanley Steamer to do away with gasoline- and diesel-powered internal-combustion engines.

Perhaps this will come in the future, but it is doubtful.

Other engineers are working on electric cars. Older people well remember the Edison and the Baker, two leaders in the electric-car field years ago. These were tiller-steered battery-powered cars often favored by maiden aunts, since they were pretty harmless as far as speed and power were concerned. Outside each window on the deluxe models of these old machines was a vase of flowers to add an elegant touch. Every

174

Dick "Dandy" Landy, drag-racing star, supertunes a modern competition engine. Note huge twin carburetors. (Chan Bush photo)

night the owner would plug the car into the house current, and by the next morning the batteries would be recharged and ready for another few miles of operation.

Still, both steam and electricity have been tried in the past, and have had only temporary success before the more reliable internal-combustion engine pushed them aside. In the intervening years, all of our technology has been directed at improving the internal-combustion type, with little thought or development of steam or electric engines. The truth is, for the jobs it is designed to do, the internal-combustion engine does the best over the long haul.

It is relatively efficient; it is as safe as can be expected; it can go for hundreds of miles without attention; and when it does need fuel or service, these are readily available. We have geared ourselves to the internal-combustion engine.

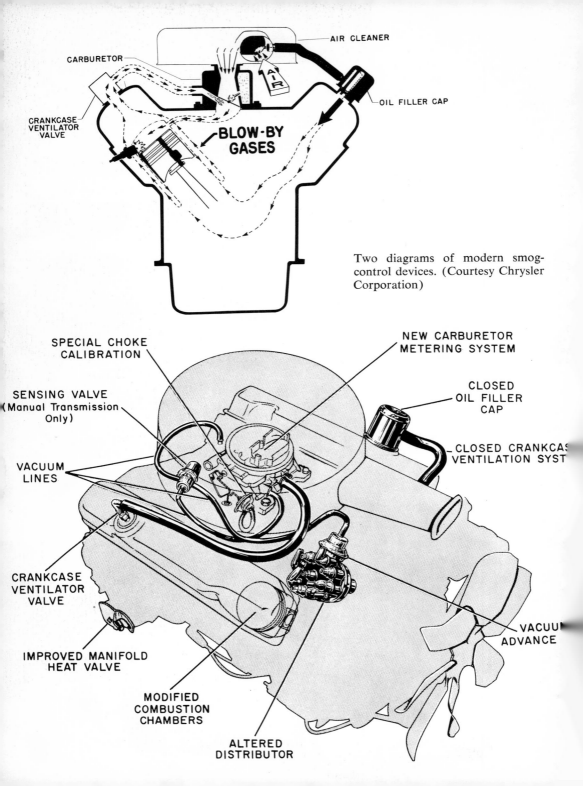

AIR CLEANER

CARBURETOR

OIL FILLER CAP

CRANKCASE
VENTILATOR
VALVE

**BLOW-BY
GASES**

Two diagrams of modern smog-
control devices. (Courtesy Chrysler
Corporation)

SPECIAL CHOKE
CALIBRATION

NEW CARBURETOR
METERING SYSTEM

SENSING VALVE
(Manual Transmission
Only)

CLOSED
OIL FILLER
CAP

CLOSED CRANKCAS
VENTILATION SYST

VACUUM
LINES

CRANKCASE
VENTILATOR
VALVE

VACUU
ADVANCE

IMPROVED MANIFOLD
HEAT VALVE

MODIFIED
COMBUSTION
CHAMBERS

ALTERED
DISTRIBUTOR

Three views of Chrysler's experimental gas-turbine automobile. Fifty of these cars were made in 1963-64, and are still being tested by selected drivers around the country.

Many scientists are working on ways to *control* the harmful emissions from internal-combustion engines. This, at present, seems the logical answer.

Perhaps in the future we will have newer, better forms of power. Atomic reaction does not produce smog (though there are certainly harmful side effects from this, also, which we will have to learn to control). "Ion" power, another possibility being investigated by scientists, could eventually replace the internal-combustion engine. Scientists foresee the day when we will buy an automobile (or whatever we might call these vehicles of the future) with fuel for the life of the machine already installed. For the want of a better name, these vehicles are being called "Transportation Pods" and will come equipped with automatic guidance devices as well as fuel, so that the driver will rarely have to steer. Yet, even in this transportation of the future, the engines will likely be a form

Some engineers suggest that electric cars are the cars of the future. This is a diagram of the Electrovair II, built by General Motors. Range is only 40 to 70 miles.

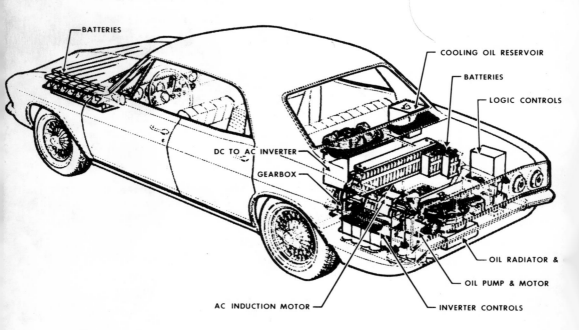

BATTERIES

COOLING OIL RESERVOIR

BATTERIES

LOGIC CONTROLS

DC TO AC INVERTER

GEARBOX

OIL RADIATOR &

OIL PUMP & MOTOR

AC INDUCTION MOTOR

INVERTER CONTROLS

Another application of modern internal-combustion engine—the world's fastest boat (spring 1968). Driven by Lee Taylor, the craft is powered by a J-46 jet engine. (Courtesy Harvey Aluminum)

of "internal combustion," for very probably we will still obtain power by converting heat energy to mechanical energy.

Meanwhile, scientists continue to work on ways to control the emissions from today's internal-combustion engines. They have developed workable "smog-control devices," which decrease the exhaust of noxious gases from an engine. Some of these devices feed the gases back through the engine for reburning; other types remove harmful materials from the gases; some burn the materials from the gases by using an "afterburner" in the exhaust system of the engine.

New fuels that, when burned, emit less harmful materials are under development. As a start, scientists suggest that burning diesel oil emits less smog-producing chemicals than burning gasoline. Turbine engines run well on these oils (or, for that matter, on almost any other kind of combustible liquid, including *perfume*). So perhaps turbines are the engine of the future, for even if they use the smog-producing fuels of today, they burn so hot that most of the harmful chemicals are consumed. And, speaking of perfume, we could make what smog is left at least smell nicer.

We know that rotary engines emit less smog-producing chemicals than reciprocating-piston internal-combustion engines, so these may be the engines of tomorrow.

Perhaps our scientists will meet with success in their effort to suppress smog from the engines we use today. Certainly conversion to either electricity or steam as the primary source of power would mean far more complicated conversions of all the related things we use (service stations, garages, airports, perhaps even streets and highways). Then, with this success, we could continue to develop the internal-combustion engine for even newer and better and more efficient devices. This is perhaps the answer for the future.

You might expect to see in the next few years turbine-powered automobiles and trucks. Several manufacturers today are producing such engines in limited numbers, and one model has been on the streets for several years being tested by selected drivers. Does this mean the end of the reciprocating-piston engine as we know it? Not necessarily, for just because one turbine is becoming available (very, very gradually) and several others are being used in racing cars, the changeover to turbines as the standard form of power would take many years. And then only if the present testing and development proves them to be better in the long run.

This is taking into full consideration the fact that racing application almost always indicates that the power source being tested will be available in the relatively near future for everybody. This is especially true when the application has moved all the way up to the Indianapolis Motor Speedway—for here was finally developed such now-standard items as the rear-view mirror, the pneumatic tire, and modern shock absorbers.

Soon may come conversions to rotary engines, for this power source shows great promise. Perhaps racing men will be the first to try these engines, after they have been basically developed into high-speed machines at company test tracks. If they succeed on race tracks, the general public will begin to ask for them in passenger cars. If they fail. . . ? Well, six-wheeled vehicles, cross-mounted and upside-down engines, and many other odd devices have been tried at race tracks, failed, and were forgotten. And many, many more will be tried.

Jet power for automobiles? Perhaps, though several knotty problems will have to be solved with this power source, including the major problem of the superheated exhaust blast on a crowded freeway. New, super-powered braking systems would also have to be developed, for the vehicles would no longer have the braking effect of the standard internal-combustion engine.

Possibly atomic power will become popular—far in the future yet, of course. This will be the engine with the built-in fuel supply. You will buy it, you will run it until it is "out of gas" (which will take years and years), and then you will scrap it.

But even this, though "pistons" and "rods" and "cylinder blocks" will have joined such words as "hand crank" and "spark advance lever" in history, will still be a form of internal-combustion engine.

Man has not yet designed and built a power source that is more efficient or more practical than the engine we know now—but the future conceals much from us. Will a better engine be invented?

index